Phaselock Techniques

The Wiley Monograph Series on Electronic Circuits

R. D. Middlebrook, SERIES EDITOR

Phaselock Techniques
Floyd M. Gardner

Differential Amplifiers
R. D. Middlebrook

Phaselock Techniques

Floyd M. Gardner, Ph.D
Consulting Engineer

John Wiley & Sons, Inc.

NEW YORK   LONDON   SYDNEY

Preface

The material in this book is intended for three groups of practicing engineers who may be confronted with phaselock problems—system designers who must know the capabilities and limitations of phaselock, equipment designers who build phaselock circuits, and equipment users who specify phaselock performance to their suppliers and who must therefore understand the operation of their equipment.

For these readers the book discusses basic principles of phaselock operation, typical practices of phaselock engineering, and selected applications of phaselock to various problems. I hope the material will be of interest and value.

Long mathematical derivations have been avoided on the premise that they are of little interest to the practicing engineer. Instead, I have tried to outline the underlying assumptions and methods employed in derivations and have stressed practical results. For those readers who may be interested in further details, I have listed numerous references.

Nonetheless, because many aspects of phaselock can be expressed only in mathematical terms, the largest part of the material is presented here in that form. As a consequence, the reader must have some mathematical background. For fullest understanding of the subject some familiarity with transfer functions in the LaPlace transform notation, a background in feedback or servo theory, and a nodding acquaintance with noise and spectral analysis of stochastic processes are needed. The results and applications are presented so that a less well-prepared reader can understand them, but the minimum prerequisites are necessary for a full understanding of the detailed basic principles.

In October of 1964 I had the opportunity to present a two-week course on phaselock techniques to a group at NASA's Marshal Space Flight Center at Huntsville, Alabama. Later, the same course was repeated at the NASA installations at Goddard Space Flight Center, at Wallop's Island, and at Houston. Course notes were prepared for the students, and this book is in some respects an outgrowth of these notes.

My thanks are due to my client, Resdel Engineering Corporation of Pasadena, California, for asking me to prepare and deliver the courses and allowing me to publish this book. Thanks are also due to the National

Aeronautics and Space Administration which sponsored the courses and
gave permission to publish. My appreciation also to Steven S. Kent and
R. D. Dasenbrock of Resdel who contributed portions of Chapters 7
and 8.

FLOYD M. GARDNER

Reseda, California
April 1966

Contents

Phaselock Techniques

Chapter One

Introduction

1-1 Nature of Phaselock

A phaselock loop contains three basic components (Figure 1-1):

1. A phase detector (PD).
2. A low-pass filter.
3. A voltage-controlled oscillator (VCO), whose frequency is controlled by an external voltage.

The phase detector compares the phase of a periodic input signal against the phase of the VCO; output of the PD is a measure of the phase difference

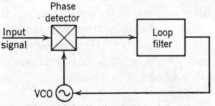

Figure 1-1   Basic phaselock loop.

between its two inputs. The difference voltage is then filtered by the loop filter and applied to the VCO. Control voltage on the VCO changes the frequency in a direction that reduces the phase difference between the input signal and the local oscillator.

When the loop is "locked," the control voltage is such that the frequency of the VCO is exactly equal to the average frequency of the input signal. For each cycle of input there is one, and only one, cycle of oscillator output. One obvious—and common—application of phaselock is in automatic frequency control (AFC). Perfect frequency control can be achieved by this method, whereas conventional AFC techniques necessarily entail some frequency error.

To maintain the control voltage needed for lock it is generally necessary to have a nonzero output from the phase detector. Consequently, the loop operates with some phase error present; as a practical matter, however, this error tends to be small in a well-designed loop.

A slightly different explanation may provide a better understanding of loop operation. Suppose that the incoming signal carries information in its phase or frequency; this signal is inevitably corrupted by additive noises. The task of a phaselock receiver is to reproduce the original signal while removing as much of the noise as possible.

To reproduce the signal the receiver makes use of a local oscillator whose frequency is very close to that expected in the signal. Local oscillator and incoming signal waveforms are compared with one another by a phase detector whose error output indicates instantaneous phase difference. To suppress noise the error is averaged over some length of time, and the averaged error is then used to control the frequency of the oscillator.

If the original signal is well behaved (stable in frequency), the local oscillator will need very little information to be able to track, and that information can be obtained by averaging for a long period of time, thereby eliminating noise that could be very large. The input to the loop is a noisy signal, whereas the output of the VCO is a cleaned-up version of the input. It is reasonable, therefore, to consider the loop as a kind of filter that passes signals and rejects noise.

Two important characteristics of the filter are that the bandwidth can be very small and the filter automatically tracks the signal frequency. These features, automatic tracking and narrow bandwidth, account for the major uses of phaselock receivers. Narrow bandwidth is capable of rejecting large amounts of noise; it is not at all unusual for a PLL to recover a signal deeply embedded in noise.

1-2   History and Application

One example of phaselock—of a sort—has been in existence for many years. Electric utilities maintain the average frequency of their generators extremely close to 60 Hz, largely so that electric clocks will not gain or lose time. Frequency is regulated by a kind of phaselock loop in which the input signal is a time of day, ultimately derived from the Bureau of Standards or the Naval Observatory. This reference time is compared against the time indicated by a clock driven by the utility's generator. The comparing device is a phase detector in fact, although not in name, and the turbine and generator constitute a VCO.

Any phase (time) discrepancy information is used to adjust the speed of the turbines in a direction that will reduce the discrepancy. Filtering comes in part from inertia of the rotating machinery and electrical inertia of the system load; however, most of the filtering comes from the scheduling of speed adjustments.

This example, in which phase comparison and frequency adjustment are performed on an intermittent basis and with disturbances coming from variations of the load rather than noise on the input signal, is perhaps somewhat strained and atypical. Nonetheless, if one were so inclined, the process could be analyzed on a phaselock basis.

Apparently the first description* of phaselock as such was published by de Bellescize [Bel-1]† in 1932 and treated the synchronous reception of radio signals. Superheterodyne receivers had come into use during the 1920's, but there was a continual search for a simpler technique; one approach investigated was the synchronous or homodyne receiver.

In essence, this receiver consists of nothing but a local oscillator, a mixer, and an audio amplifier. To operate, the oscillator has to be adjusted to exactly the same frequency as the carrier of the incoming signal which is then converted to an intermediate frequency of exactly zero Hz. Output of the mixer contains demodulated information that is carried as sidebands by the signal. Interference will not be synchronous with the local oscillator, and therefore mixer output caused by an interfering signal is a beat note that can be suppressed by audio filtering.

Correct tuning of the local oscillator is essential to synchronous reception; any frequency error whatsoever will hopelessly garble the information. Furthermore, phase of the local oscillator must agree, within a fairly small fraction of a cycle, with the received carrier phase. In other words, the local oscillator must be phaselocked to the incoming signal.

For various reasons the simple synchronous receiver has never been used extensively. Present-day phaselock receivers almost invariably use the superheterodyne principle and tend to be highly complex. One of their most important applications is in the reception of the very weak signals from distant spacecraft.

The first widespread use of phaselock came in the synchronization of horizontal and vertical scan in television receivers [Wen-1]. The start of each line and of each interlaced half-frame of a television picture are signaled by a pulse transmitted with the video information. As a very crude approach to reconstructing a scan raster on the TV tube, these pulses can be stripped off and individually utilized to trigger a pair of single-sweep generators.

---

* Existence of this original paper was recently brought to light by T. J. Rey [Rey-2].

† Citations indicate references listed at the end of this book.

A slightly more sophisticated approach uses a pair of free-running relaxation oscillators to drive the sweep generators. In this way sweep is present even if synchronization is absent. Free-running frequencies of the oscillators are set a small amount below the horizontal and vertical pulse rates, and the stripped pulses are used to trigger the oscillators prematurely and thus to synchronize them to the line and half-frame rates (half-frame because U.S. standard television interlaces the lines on alternate vertical scans).

In the absence of noise this scheme can provide good synchronization and is entirely adequate. Unfortunately, noise is rarely absent, and any triggering circuit is particularly susceptible to it. As an extreme, triggered scan will completely fail at a signal-to-noise ratio that still provides a recognizable though inferior picture.

Under less extreme conditions noise will cause starting-time jitter and occasional misfiring far out of phase. Horizontal jitter reduces horizontal resolution and causes vertical lines to have a ragged appearance. Severe horizontal misfiring will usually cause a narrow, horizontal black streak to appear.

Vertical jitter causes an apparent vertical movement of the picture. Also, the interlaced lines of successive half-frames would so move with respect to one another that further picture degradation would result.

Noise fluctuation can be vastly reduced by phaselocking the two oscillators to the stripped sync pulses. Instead of triggering on each pulse, a phaselock technique examines the relative phase between each oscillator and many of its sync pulses and adjusts oscillator frequency so that the average phase discrepancy is small. Because it looks at many pulses, a phaselock synchronizer is not confused by occasional large noise pulses that disrupt a triggered synchronizer. The flywheel synchronizers in present-day TV receivers are really phaselocked loops. The name "flywheel" is used partly because the circuit is able to coast through periods of increased noise or weak signal. Substantial improvement in synchronizing performance is obtained by phaselock.

Space use of phaselock began with the launching of the first American artificial satellites. These vehicles carried low-power (10 mw) CW transmitters; received signals were correspondingly weak. Because of Doppler shift and drift of the transmitting oscillator, there was considerable uncertainty about the exact frequency of the received signal. At the 108-MHz frequency originally used the Doppler shift could range over a ± 3-kHz interval.

With an ordinary, fixed-tuned receiver, bandwidth would therefore have to be at least 6 kHz, if not more. However, the signal itself occupies a very narrow spectrum, and could be contained in something like a 6-Hz bandwidth.

Noise power in the receiver is directly proportional to bandwidth. Therefore, if conventional techniques were used, a noise penalty of 1000 times (30 db) would have to be accepted. (The numbers have become even more spectacular as technology has progressed; transmission frequencies have moved up to S-band, making the Doppler range some ±75 kHz, whereas receiver bandwidths as small as 3 Hz have been achieved. The penalty for conventional techniques would thus be about 47 db). Such penalties are intolerable and that is why narrow-band, phaselocked, tracking receivers are used.

Noise can be rejected by a narrow-band filter, but if the filter is fixed the signal will almost never be within the passband. For a narrow filter to be usable it must be capable of tracking the signal. A phaselocked loop is capable of providing both the narrow bandwidth and the tracking that are needed. Moreover, extremely narrow bandwidths can be conveniently obtained (3 to 1000 Hz are typical for space applications); if necessary, bandwidth is easily changed.

For a Doppler signal the information needed to determine vehicle velocity is the Doppler frequency shift. A phaselock receiver is well-adapted to Doppler recovery, for it has no frequency error when locked. (The effect of phase errors is covered in later chapters.)

1-3 Other Applications

The following applications, further discussed in Chapter 8 represent some of the current uses of phaselock.

1. One method of tracking moving vehicles involves transmitting a coherent signal to the vehicle, offsetting the signal frequency, and re-transmitting back to the ground. The "coherent transponder" in the vehicle must operate so that the input and output frequencies are exactly related in the ratio m/n, where m and n are integers. Phaselock techniques are often used to establish coherence.

2. A phaselocked loop can be used as a frequency demodulator, in which service it has superior performance to a conventional discriminator.

3. Noisy oscillators can be enclosed in a loop and locked to a clean signal. If the loop has wide bandwidth, the oscillator tracks out its own noise and its output is greatly cleaned up.

4. Frequency multipliers and dividers can be built by using PLL's.

5. Bit synchronization of PCM telemetry transmission is typically obtained by phaselock methods.

As for the future, it would appear that phaselock will find use in the communications applications of lasers. One of the major advantages of lasers is their coherence; however, unless a coherent receiver (rather than a simple power detector) can be used, much of the benefit of coherence is lost. A method of phaselocking two lasers has recently been described [Enl-1].

1-4 Organization of Book

A certain amount of mathematics and network theory background is needed for an adequate understanding of phaselock and therefore a very brief summary and review of the pertinent material is presented in Appendix A.

In Chapter 2 the basic loop is described and its fundamental equations (assuming linear operation) are derived. Various types of loop and their respective peculiarities are discussed. Phaselock loops are often intended to operate in the presence of considerable noise. Chapter 3 investigates their performance in noise and the amount of noise needed to make them fail.

Because a locked oscillator must track the input signal, Chapter 4 discusses how well the oscillator tracks if input frequency is not constant, how severe the input variation may be without loss of lock, and how the loop may be brought into lock initially.

Chapter 5 is a survey of the operation and circuits of some of the loop components whereas Chapter 6 touches briefly on the problem of optimum loop design. Chapter 7 is concerned with the principles and designs of phaselock receivers, and Chapter 8 covers other applications of phaselock.

Finally, Chapter 9 considers methods of testing phaselock receivers and other phaselock equipment.

Following the last chapter are lists of the nomenclature used in the text and references cited. Also, an extensive bibliography has been compiled. A list of important formulas is included as a summary and aid to equipment designers.

Chapter Two

Loop fundamentals

2-1 Basic Transfer Functions

Consider an elementary loop consisting of a phase detector (PD), a low-pass loop filter, and a voltage-controlled oscillator (VCO). The input signal has a phase of $\theta_i(t)$, and the VCO output has a phase $\theta_o(t)$. For the present it is assumed that the loop is locked, that the phase detector is linear (this assumption is both justified and qualified in Chapter 3), and

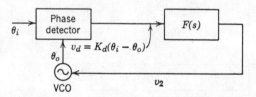

Figure 2-1 Basic loop block diagram.

that the PD output voltage is proportional to the difference in phase between its inputs; that is,

$$v_d = K_d(\theta_i - \theta_o) \qquad (2\text{-}1)$$

where K_d is called the "phase-detector gain factor" and has dimensions of volts per radian.

Phase error voltage is filtered by the low-pass loop filter. Noise and high-frequency signal components are suppressed; also, the filter helps to determine dynamic performance of the loop. Filter transfer function is given by $F(s)$.

Frequency of the voltage-controlled oscillator (VCO) is controlled by the filtered error voltage v_2. Deviation of the VCO from its center frequency is $\Delta\omega = K_o v_2$, where K_o is the VCO gain constant and has dimensions of radians per second per volt. Since frequency is the derivative of phase, the VCO operation may be described as $d\theta_o/dt = K_o v_2$. By taking Laplace

7

transforms we obtain

$$L\left[\frac{d\theta_o(t)}{dt}\right] = s\theta_o(s) = K_o\,V_2(s) \tag{2-2}$$

therefore

$$\theta_o(s) = \frac{K_o V_2(s)}{s}$$

In other words, the phase of the VCO output will be proportional to the integral of the input control voltage.

By using Laplace notation the following equations are applicable:

$$V_d(s) = K_d[\theta_i(s) - \theta_o(s)] \tag{2-3}$$

$$V_2(s) = F(s)\,V_d(s) \tag{2-4}$$

$$\theta_o(s) = \frac{K_o\,V_2(s)}{s} \tag{2-5}$$

Combination of these equations results in the basic loop equations

$$\frac{\theta_o(s)}{\theta_i(s)} = H(s) = \frac{K_o K_d\,F(s)}{s + K_o K_d\,F(s)} \tag{2-6}$$

$$\frac{\theta_i(s) - \theta_o(s)}{\theta_i(s)} = \frac{\theta_e(s)}{\theta_i(s)} = \frac{s}{s + K_o K_d\,F(s)} \tag{2-7}$$

Before proceeding, it is necessary to specify the loop filter $F(s)$.

2-2   Second-Order Loop

Two widely used loop filters are shown with their respective transfer functions in Figure 2-2. The passive filter is quite simple and often satisfactory for many purposes. The active filter requires a high-gain d-c amplifier but provides better tracking performance, as shown in Chapter 4.

For the passive filter the loop transfer function is

$$H_1(s) = \frac{K_o K_d(s\tau_2 + 1)/(\tau_1 + \tau_2)}{s^2 + s(1 + K_o K_d\tau_2)/(\tau_1 + \tau_2) + K_o K_d/(\tau_1 + \tau_2)}$$

For the active filter

$$H_2(s) = \frac{K_o K_d(s\tau_2 + 1)/\tau_1}{s^2 + s(K_o K_d\tau_2/\tau_1) + K_o K_d/\tau_1}$$

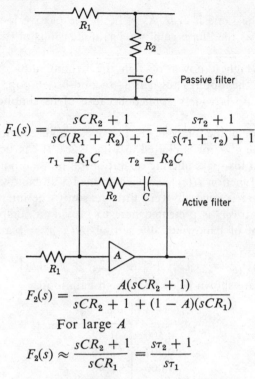

$$F_1(s) = \frac{sCR_2 + 1}{sC(R_1 + R_2) + 1} = \frac{s\tau_2 + 1}{s(\tau_1 + \tau_2) + 1}$$

$$\tau_1 = R_1C \qquad \tau_2 = R_2C$$

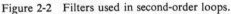

$$F_2(s) = \frac{A(sCR_2 + 1)}{sCR_2 + 1 + (1 - A)(sCR_1)}$$

For large A

$$F_2(s) \approx \frac{sCR_2 + 1}{sCR_1} = \frac{s\tau_2 + 1}{s\tau_1}$$

Figure 2-2   Filters used in second-order loops.

provided that amplifier gain is very large. These transfer functions may be rewritten as

$$H_1(s) = \frac{s(2\zeta\omega_n - \omega_n^2/K_oK_d) + \omega_n^2}{s^2 + 2\zeta\omega_ns + \omega_n^2} = \frac{s\omega_n(2\zeta - \omega_n/K_oK_d) + \omega_n^2}{s^2 + 2\zeta\omega_ns + \omega_n^2} \qquad (2\text{-}8)$$

$$H_2(s) = \frac{2\zeta\omega_ns + \omega_n^2}{s^2 + 2\zeta\omega_ns + \omega_n^2} \qquad (2\text{-}9)$$

in which, drawing on servo terminology, ω_n is the "natural frequency" of the loop and ζ is the "damping factor." Observe that the two transfer

Passive filter	Active filter
$\omega_n = \left(\dfrac{K_oK_d}{\tau_1 + \tau_2}\right)^{1/2}$	$\omega_n = \left(\dfrac{K_oK_d}{\tau_1}\right)^{1/2}$
$\zeta = \dfrac{1}{2}\left(\dfrac{K_oK_d}{\tau_1 + \tau_2}\right)^{1/2}\left(\tau_2 + \dfrac{1}{K_oK_d}\right)$	$\zeta = \dfrac{\tau_2}{2}\left(\dfrac{K_oK_d}{\tau_1}\right)^{1/2}$

$(2\text{-}10)$

functions are the same if $\omega_n/K_oK_d \ll 2\zeta$ in the passive loop. The factor K_oK_d is known as the "loop gain"; it has dimensions of $(time)^{-1}$, that is, frequency.

Because the highest power of s in the denominator of the transfer function is two, the loop is known as a "second-order loop." This form of second-order loop is widely applied because of its simplicity and good performance.

The magnitude of the frequency response of a high-gain loop for several values of damping factor is plotted in Figure 2-3. It can be seen that the loop performs a low-pass filtering operation on phase inputs.

The transfer function $H(s)$ has a well-defined 3-db bandwidth which we label ω_{3db}. There is generally very little reason to be interested in ω_{3db}, but its relation to ω_n is presented here to provide a comparison with a familiar concept of bandwidth. By setting $|H(j\omega)|^2 = \frac{1}{2}$ and solving for ω we find that

$$\omega_{3db} = \omega_n[2\zeta^2 + 1 + \sqrt{(2\zeta^2 + 1)^2 + 1}]^{\frac{1}{2}}$$

Typical values are shown below for a high-gain loop.

ζ	ω_{3db}/ω_n
0.500	1.82
0.707	2.06
1.000	2.48

Error response of the loop is also of interest. For a high-gain, second-order loop the error response is

$$\frac{\theta_e(s)}{\theta_i(s)} = 1 - H(s) = \frac{s^2}{s^2 + 2\zeta\omega_n s + \omega_n^2} \qquad (2\text{-}11)$$

whereas for a low-gain loop

$$\frac{\theta_e(s)}{\theta_i(s)} = \frac{s(s + \omega_n^2/K_oK_d)}{s^2 + 2\zeta\omega_n s + \omega_n^2} = \frac{s[s + 1/(\tau_1 + \tau_2)]}{s^2 + 2\zeta\omega_n s + \omega_n^2} \qquad (2\text{-}12)$$

Error response is plotted in Figure 2-4 for a high-gain loop with $\zeta = 0.707$. A high-pass characteristic is obtained; that is the loop tracks low-frequency changes but cannot track high frequencies.

2-3   Other Loop Types

A first-order loop is obtained if the filter is omitted entirely; that is, $F(s) = 1$. The loop transfer function is of the form

$$H(s) = \frac{K_oK_d}{s + K_oK_d} \qquad (2\text{-}13)$$

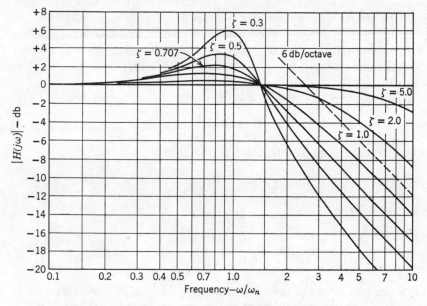

Figure 2-3   Frequency response; high-gain, second-order loop.

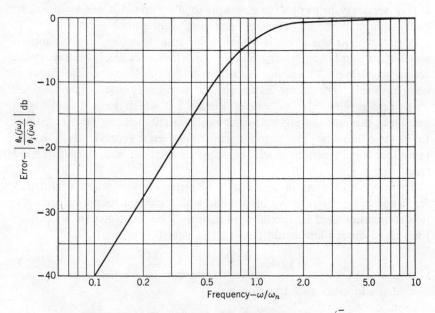

Figure 2-4   Error response of high-gain loop, $\zeta = \sqrt{2}/2$.

so that loop gain (K_oK_d) is the only parameter available to the designer for adjustment. If it is necessary to have large loop gain (often needed to ensure good tracking), the bandwidth must also be large. Therefore narrow bandwidth and good tracking are incompatible in the first-order loop; for this reason it is not often used unless a very wide bandwidth is wanted.

A second-order loop results if a filter

$$F(s) = \frac{1}{s\tau + 1} \tag{2-14}$$

is used. The loop transfer function is therefore

$$H(s) = \frac{K_oK_d/\tau}{s^2 + s/\tau + K_oK_d/\tau} \tag{2-15}$$

whence

$$\omega_n = \left(\frac{K_oK_d}{\tau}\right)^{1/2}$$

$$\zeta = \frac{1}{2}\left(\frac{1}{\tau K_oK_d}\right)^{1/2} \tag{2-16}$$

There are two circuit parameters available (τ and K_oK_d), whereas usually three loop parameter specifications must be met (ω_n, ζ, and K_oK_d). Obviously, the three loop parameters cannot be chosen independently. If it is necessary to have large gain and small bandwidth, the loop will be badly underdamped and transient response will be poor.

A very similar condition is found in servomechanisms; in the simplest servos damping becomes very small as gain increases. The solution to the servo problem is to employ tachometer feedback or to use lag-lead compensation. The latter expedient is commonly used in phaselock loops and results in the filters of Figure 2-2 which have already been analyzed. Because the lag-lead filter has two independent time constants the natural frequency and damping can be chosen independently. Furthermore, loop gain can be made as large as may be necessary for good tracking.

There are situations in which a third-order loop provides useful performance characteristics not obtainable with a simpler loop. Accordingly, it is sometimes used in special applications. The most general loop filter for a third-order loop would have the transfer function

$$F(s) = \frac{(s\tau_2 + 1)(s\tau_4 + 1)}{(s\tau_1 + 1)(s\tau_3 + 1)} \tag{2-17}$$

so that the loop transfer function is

$$H(s) = \frac{K_oK_d(s\tau_2 + 1)(s\tau_4 + 1)}{s^3\tau_1\tau_3 + s^2(\tau_1 + \tau_3 + K_oK_d\tau_2\tau_4) + s[1 + K_oK_d(\tau_2 + \tau_4)] + K_oK_d} \tag{2-18}$$

It will be seen in Chapter 4 that the third-order loop is most useful if the two poles of its loop filter are at the origin, that is, if the loop filter contains two cascaded integrators. In that case the transfer function of the loop filter is

$$F(s) = \frac{(s\tau_2 + 1)(s\tau_4 + 1)}{s^2\tau_1\tau_2} \qquad (2\text{-}19)$$

and the loop transfer function becomes

$$H(s) = \frac{K_o K_d(s\tau_2 + 1)(s\tau_4 + 1)}{s^3\tau_1\tau_3 + s^2 K_o K_d\tau_2\tau_4 + s K_o K_d(\tau_2 + \tau_4) + K_o K_d} \qquad (2\text{-}20)$$

To our knowledge there has never been a loop constructed with an order higher than third. One reason would seem to be that there has been no need for higher-order loops in the applications in which phaselock techniques are most commonly employed. Also, the closed-loop parameters of high-order, active networks tend to be overly sensitive to changes of gain and circuit components. Finally, it is more difficult to stabilize a high-order loop, whereas the second-order loop (as commonly built) is unconditionally stable.

2-4 Root-Locus Plots

A considerable degree of insight into the behavior of a phaselocked loop can be attained by determining the locations of the poles of the closed-loop response. These poles change their locations as the loop gain is changed. The path that the poles trace out in their migrations in the complex s-plane is known as the root-locus plot. A major advantage of the root-locus method is that the plot can be determined graphically and relatively quickly by working solely from the locations of the known open-loop poles and zeros and utilizing a few simple rules.*

Typically, the locus is drawn for the full range of gain variation, from zero to infinity. The plot starts (zero gain) on the open-loop poles and terminates (infinite gain) on the open-loop zeros (some of which may be located at infinity). Open-loop transfer function for any PLL is

$$\frac{K_o K_d F(s)}{s} \qquad (2\text{-}21)$$

Thus open-loop poles always include one at the origin besides the poles of $F(s)$. The open-loop zeros are the zeros of $F(s)$ and a zero at infinity due to the $1/s$ term.

* For an extensive description of root-locus methods see J. G. Truxal, *Automatic Feedback Control System Synthesis*, Chapter 4, McGraw-Hill, New York, 1955.

As might be expected, the first-order loop has the simplest root locus. There is a single pole at the origin, a single zero at infinity, and the closed-loop pole moves along the negative real axis from zero to infinity as the gain increases.

A second-order loop, which uses only a lag filter (2-14), has two open-

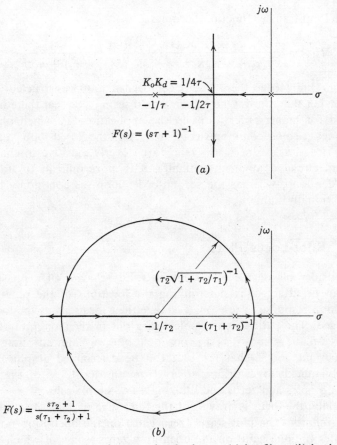

(a)

(b)

Figure 2-5 Root-locus plots for second-order loops; (a) lag filter; (b) lag-lead filter.

loop poles, one at zero and one at $s = -1/\tau$, and two zeros at infinity. The root locus is sketched in Figure 2-5a. Initially, the poles move toward each other on the negative real axis. When they meet halfway, they become a complex conjugate pair and move toward infinity along a vertical line at $s = -\dfrac{1}{2\tau}$. It may be seen that damping becomes very small as gain increases.

The benefit obtainable from a lead term may be seen in Figure 2-5b. Here, too, the poles migrate together and become complex when they meet. However, because of the finite zero, the complex portion of the locus is now a circle centered at $-1/\tau_2$. Damping will be small for moderately small gains, but beyond a minimum point damping increases with increasing gain. With sufficiently high gain, the locus eventually returns to the real axis and the loop is overdamped. One branch of the locus terminates at the finite zero; the other terminates at infinity.

The plot of Figure 2-5b is for a passive loop filter. If the loop filter were a perfect integrator (an idealized active filter), both poles would originate at the origin, and the diameter of the circle would be $1/\tau_2$. Otherwise the plot would be little altered.

It is common practice to design second-order loops with a damping factor $\zeta = 1/\sqrt{2} = 0.707$, in which case the closed-loop poles would be on radial lines located at ± 45 degrees from the negative real axis. With an active filter, for which the root-locus circle passes through the origin of the s-plane, these poles would be located at $1/\tau_2 \, (-1 \pm j1)$. Thus the poles are located on the same vertical line as the zeros; furthermore, $\omega_n = \sqrt{2}/\tau_2$. Similarly, if $\zeta = \frac{1}{2}$, it turns out that $\omega_n = 1/\tau_2$, and a circle of radius $1/\tau_2$ centered at the origin passes through both poles and the zero. If $\zeta = 1$, the poles are coincident on the negative real axis and $\omega_n = 2/\tau_2$. These facts are easily seen on a root-locus plot but are by no means obvious with a purely analytic approach.

A third-order loop has two zeros and two poles in its loop filter, which leaves four parameter choices open to the designer. It is shown in Chapter 4 that the third-order loop is most useful if both filter poles are at the origin. Purely for convenience we also assume that the zeros are coincident at $s = -1/\tau_2$. Figure 2-6 shows the root locus of this specific loop. Because it is especially easy to compute and plot this particular locus, it was chosen for illustration*; however, the general characteristics of the plot are fairly typical of any third-order loop that would be considered useful.

One feature of the plot is very striking: the locus enters the right half-plane for low values of gain, and the loop will be unstable for that condition. This is in direct contrast to the first- and second-order loops which were unconditionally stable for all values of gain. When a third-order loop is used, the gain must be prevented from falling into the unstable region.

---

* Furthermore, several designers of third-order loops have chosen this configuration in their practical designs.

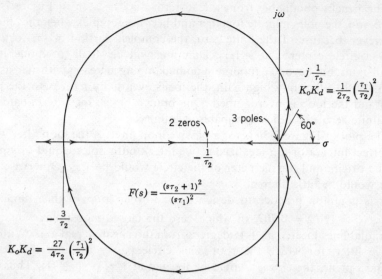

Figure 2-6   Root locus plot of third-order loop.

Chapter Three

Noise performance

3-1 Linear Analysis

Consider the phase detector to be a perfect multiplier with two inputs $e_1(t)$ and $e_2(t)$. Its output is $K_m e_1 e_2$, where K_m is a constant.

Now suppose the signal input is

$$v_i(t) = V_s \sin(\omega_i t + \theta_i)$$

and the VCO waveform* is

$$v_o(t) = V_o \cos(\omega_i t + \theta_o)$$

Output of the phase detector (neglecting double-frequency terms that will be removed by the loop filter) is

$$v_d = \frac{V_s V_o K_m}{2} \sin(\theta_i - \theta_o) \tag{3-1}$$

The linearizing approximation invariably made requires that $(\theta_i - \theta_o)$ be small and that the relation

$$\sin(\theta_i - \theta_o) \approx (\theta_i - \theta_o)$$

be used. For this approximation phase detector output is

$$v_d \approx \frac{K_m V_s V_o}{2} (\theta_i - \theta_o) \tag{3-2}$$

In terms of earlier notation, the phase detector gain constant is

$$K_d = \frac{K_m V_s V_o}{2} \tag{3-3}$$

---

* Note that v_i and v_o are really 90 degrees out of phase with one another. The input has been written as a sine, and the VCO output as a cosine. The two phases θ_i and θ_o are referred to these quadrature references.

which is a function of input-signal level. Therefore, if the input-signal amplitude varies, K_d and all loop parameters dependent on loop gain will also vary.

Suppose the input to the loop consists of a sinusoidal signal plus narrowband gaussian noise.

$$v_i(t) = V_s \sin{(\omega_i t + \theta_i)} + n(t) \tag{3-4}$$

As shown in Appendix A, the noise may be expanded as

$$n(t) = n_c(t) \cos{\omega_i t} - n_s(t) \sin{\omega_i(t)} \tag{3-5}$$

This noise is then multiplied in the phase detector by the VCO waveform, and the noise output of the phase detector is (discarding double-frequency terms)

$$v_{dn}(t) = \frac{K_m V_o}{2} \left[n_c(t) \cos{\theta_o} + n_s(t) \sin{\theta_o} \right] \tag{3-6}$$

To obtain simple results the approximation is made that θ_o is independent of $n(t)$. This approximation is reasonable if θ_o is changing slowly, compared with the input noise. Such conditions obtain if phase error due to noise is small and loop bandwidth is narrow compared with input bandwidth. This assumption of independence cannot be strictly true. Nonetheless, it proves to be a useful approximation and is applied here.

After application of the approximation, the mean-square noise output from the phase detector is found to be

$$\overline{v_{dn}^2(t)} = \left(\frac{K_m V_o}{2} \right)^2 \overline{\left[n_c^2(t) \cos^2{\theta_o} + n_s^2(t) \sin^2{\theta_o} + 2 n_c(t)\, n_s(t) \sin{\theta_o} \cos{\theta_o} \right]}$$

Since the average of a sum is the sum of the averages of the individual terms, each term within the brackets may be averaged separately. Because of the independence of $n(t)$ and θ_o, the third term may be written

$$\overline{2 n_c(t)\, n_s(t)}\ \overline{\sin{\theta_o} \cos{\theta_o}}.$$

In Appendix A it is stated that n_c and n_s are independent and therefore $\overline{n_c n_s} = \bar{n}_c \bar{n}_s$. The noise terms have zero mean so that the third term in the bracket must be zero.

The first two terms reduce to the form $\overline{n_c^2(t)}\ \overline{\cos^2{\theta_o}} + \overline{n_s^2(t)}\ \overline{\sin^2{\theta_o}}$; but $\overline{n_c^2(t)} = \overline{n_s^2(t)} = \overline{n^2(t)}$, and the sum of the first two terms becomes $\overline{n^2(t)} \left(\overline{\cos^2{\theta_o} + \sin^2{\theta_o}} \right) = \overline{n^2(t)}$, since $\sin^2{x} + \cos^2{x} = 1$. Therefore

$$\overline{v_{dn}^2(t)} = \left(\frac{K_m V_o}{2} \right)^2 \overline{n^2(t)} \tag{3-7}$$

and the rms noise output from the PD is

$$\left[\overline{v_{dn}^{2}(t)}\right]^{1/2} = \frac{K_m V_o}{2}\left[\overline{n^2(t)}\right]^{1/2} \qquad (3\text{-}7a)$$

Let us now determine the equivalent phase jitter in the input signal that would give the same rms noise output from the phase detector. Denote the mean-square input phase jitter as $\overline{\theta_{ni}^{2}}$ and consider θ_{ni} to be additive to θ_i. From (3-2) rms phase-detector output would then be $\frac{1}{2}K_m V_s V_o(\overline{\theta_{ni}^{2}})^{1/2}$.

Equating this expression to (3-7a) and solving, we obtain an equivalent input phase variance of

$$\boxed{\overline{\theta_{ni}^{2}} = \frac{\overline{n^2(t)}}{V_s^{2}} = \frac{P_n}{2P_s}\,(\text{radians})^2} \qquad (3\text{-}8)$$

where P_s is the input signal power, and P_n is the total noise power in the input.

Consider that the loop is preceded by an input bandpass filter with a rectangular shape of bandwidth B_i Hz and center frequency $f_i = \omega_i/2\pi$. (All passbands and spectra are taken as one-sided.) If the spectrum of $n(t)$ is flat within the input bandwidth, the input spectral density is

$$N_i = \frac{\overline{n^2(t)}}{B_i}\,(\text{volts})^2/\text{Hz} \qquad (3\text{-}9)$$

Spectrum of the equivalent input phase noise θ_{ni} is a low-pass rectangle with bandwidth $B_i/2$ and a density of

$$\Phi = \frac{\overline{\theta_{ni}^{2}}}{B_i/2} = \frac{2N_i}{V_s^{2}}\,(\text{radians})^2/\text{Hz} \qquad (3\text{-}10)$$

If the input power spectral density is W_i watts/Hz, the phase spectral density is

$$\Phi = \frac{W_i}{P_s}\,(\text{radians})^2/\text{Hz} \qquad (3\text{-}10a)$$

Output phase jitter (fluctuation of VCO phase) is the input phase, modified by the closed-loop transfer function $H(j\omega)$. Specifically, mean-square output phase jitter is

$$\overline{\theta_{no}^{2}} = \int_0^{B_i/2}\Phi\,|H(j\omega)|^2\,df \approx \Phi\int_0^{\infty}|H(j\omega)|^2\,df \qquad (3\text{-}11)$$

where the approximation is valid if the input bandwidth is much wider than the loop bandwidth (as defined below). For a high-gain, second-order loop

$$\overline{\theta_{no}^2} = \frac{\Phi}{2\pi j} \int_{j0}^{j\infty} \left| \frac{2\zeta\omega_n s + \omega_n^2}{s^2 + 2\zeta\omega_n s + \omega_n^2} \right|^2 ds$$

$$= \frac{\Phi}{2\pi} \int_0^\infty \frac{\omega_n^2(4\zeta^2\omega^2 + \omega_n^2)\, d\omega}{\omega_n^4 + 2\omega_n^2\omega^2(2\zeta^2 - 1) + \omega^4} \qquad (3\text{-}11a)$$

This integral may be evaluated by reference to published tables (e.g.,

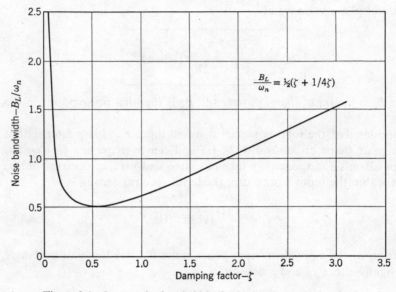

$$\frac{B_L}{\omega_n} = \tfrac{1}{2}(\zeta + 1/4\zeta)$$

Noise bandwidth—B_L/ω_n

Damping factor—ζ

Figure 3-1   Loop-noise bandwidth (for high-gain, second-order loop.)

G. Petit Bois, *Tables of Indefinite Integrals*, Dover, New York, 1961). The result is the "loop-noise bandwidth" (of the second-order loop)

$$B_L = \int_0^\infty |H(j\omega)|^2\, df = \frac{\omega_n}{2}\left(\zeta + \frac{1}{4\zeta}\right) \text{ Hz} \qquad (3\text{-}12)$$

which has dimensions of *cycles* per second, despite the fact that dimensions of ω_n are in *radians* per second. The loop-noise bandwidth, as used here, is one-sided.

Loop-noise bandwidth B_L as a function of damping is plotted in Figure 3-1. There is a minimum for $\zeta = \tfrac{1}{2}$, in which case $B_L/\omega_n = \tfrac{1}{2}$. For the very common damping of $\zeta = 0.707$, $B_L/\omega_n = 3/4\sqrt{2} = 0.53$. Between the limits of $0.25 < \zeta < 1.0$ the loop bandwidth never exceeds its minimum value by more than 25 per cent (equivalent to 1-db noise power).

When the integral of (3-11) is replaced by B_L and (3-8) to (3-10) are used, mean-square output phase jitter is

$$
\begin{aligned}
\overline{\theta_{no}^2} &= \Phi B_L = 2\overline{\theta_{ni}^2}\frac{B_L}{B_i} \\
&= \frac{P_n}{P_s}\frac{B_L}{B_i} = \frac{W_i B_L}{P_s}
\end{aligned}
\tag{3-13}
$$

This expression is valid if the rms phase jitter of the output is less than approximately 13 degrees [Mar-3]. Nonlinear behavior at high noise conditions is treated later.

Signal-to-noise ratio in the input bandwidth is

$$
(\text{SNR})_i = \frac{P_s}{P_n} = \frac{1}{2\overline{\theta_{ni}^2}}
\tag{3-14}
$$

We would like a similar and analogous relation between output phase and loop signal-to-noise ratio; that is,

$$
\overline{\theta_{no}^2} = \frac{1}{2(\text{SNR})_L}
\tag{3-15}
$$

which leads to the *definition*

$$
(\text{SNR})_L = \frac{(\text{SNR})_i B_i}{2B_L} = \frac{P_s}{2B_L W_i}
\tag{3-16}
$$

A logical oddity arises from this definition; (3-16) is the definition of $(\text{SNR})_L$ for any value of signal-to-noise ratio, high or low. However, (3-15), which was used in arriving at the definition, is a valid approximation only for $(\text{SNR})_L > 10$. Further discussion of the relation between phase jitter and $(\text{SNR})_L$ occurs later in this chapter.

It must also be observed that (3-16) is a somewhat arbitrary definition and is not unique.* Therefore, due caution should be exercized in attempting to assign physical meaning to $(\text{SNR})_L$. Signal-to-noise ratio in a loop

---

* An alternative definition, sometimes encountered, is that $(\text{SNR}) = P_s/B_L W_i$. For this definition the expression for output phase jitter must be changed accordingly.

lacks the same clearly discernible physical meaning that it would have in, for example, an IF amplifier.

Nevertheless, it is convenient to think of the loop as providing a bandpass filter action around the received signal. The filter is centered at the frequency of the signal and has a noise bandwidth of B_L on each side of center for a total equivalent input bandwidth of $2B_L$. Thus for white noise of spectral density W_i the total noise which enters the loop is $2B_L W_i$.

The arguments presented in this section for the second-order loop are equally applicable to a loop of any order. A noise bandwidth, B_L, may be defined for any finite-bandwidth loop, and (3-13), (3-15), and (3-16) may be applied directly to determine phase variance and loop SNR.

In a first-order loop the noise bandwidth is easily found to be

$$B_L = \frac{K_o K_d}{4} \text{ Hz}$$

For the third-order loop of Chapter 2, in which open-loop zeros are coincident and gain is chosen so that two of the closed-loop poles are coincident, noise bandwidth is $B_L = 2.23/\tau_2$ Hz. For other loop types B_L must be calculated from

$$B_L = \int_0^\infty |H(j\omega)|^2 \, df \text{ Hz}$$

Such an integration may be aided by referring to the appendix of *Theory of Servomechanisms* (James, Nichols, and Phillips Vol. 25 of the Radiation Laboratory Series, McGraw-Hill, New York, 1948). Values of the integral have been worked out as functions of the coefficients of the polynomials contained in $H(j\omega)$ for orders one to seven.

3-2   Noise Threshold

Output phase jitter increases as the noise-to-signal ratio increases. A phase detector has only a limited range of operation; if the phase error exceeds this range, the loop will drop out of lock.

Phase error due to noise is a fluctuating statistical quantity and is described by its rms value; however, noise peaks can greatly exceed the rms. For this reason there is always some probability that the phase-detector limits will be exceeded, no matter how small the noise. This probability is negligible for strong signals but becomes progressively larger as noise increases. Because sufficiently large noise will greatly increase the probability of exceeding the phase-detector limits, it becomes impossible to hold the loop in lock.

Practical experience shows [Mar-3] that lock cannot be held below 0-db signal-to-noise ratio in the loop. Actually, at this SNR the loop is in lock only part of the time, and any additional disturbance will tend to cause complete loss of lock.

It is nearly impossible to acquire lock if $(SNR)_L = 0$ db. In general, $(SNR)_L$ of 6 db is needed for acquisition. Martin [Mar-3] indicates that if the frequency of the incoming signal is well known acquisition at $(SNR)_L = 3$ db is practicable. The question of acquisition behavior is considered in more detail later.

If modulation or transient phase error is present, a higher signal-to-noise ratio is needed to acquire and hold lock. No simple rule describes the necessary increase of SNR; the form of the modulation will determine the amount of degradation. Even if the form is known, analytical techniques developed so far are engineering approximations and not mathematically rigorous. Several of these techniques are touched on in later chapters.

It is common practice to use the concept of "loop threshold," for which the most general definition is "that value of loop signal-to-noise ratio, below which desired performance cannot be obtained." Threshold is not defined until the criterion of performance is defined first. The most obvious performance criterion to choose is loss of lock. However, as already noted, "holding lock" can be defined only in a statistical sense inasmuch as a loop remains "in-lock" for some short period of time, even for high noise conditions.

If satisfactory statistical criteria were to be defined, a more formidable barrier to analytical derivation of a threshold criterion would still remain. Loop behavior is nonlinear, and mathematical tools for nonlinear analysis are generally inadequate for the phaselock loop. Nonetheless, there has been work that sheds considerable light on the problem.

Develet [Dev-1, 2], who derived an "absolute" unlock threshold, assumes that the phase-detector nonlinearity can be approximated by considering effective phase-detector gain to be dependent on the loop signal-to-noise ratio. His conclusion is that the loop unlocks if loop SNR falls below $+1.34$ db. At this threshold level the rms phase jitter is calculated to be 1.0 radian. This result shows reasonably good agreement with Martin's empirical approximation [Mar-3] that unlock threshold is close to 0 db, at which condition phase jitter is 1 radian rms.

A different threshold criterion may be defined as that value of loop SNR for which the output phase fluctuation exceeds some prescribed value. To make use of this criterion it is necessary to know the behavior of $\overline{\theta_{no}{}^2}$ as a function of $(SNR)_L$.

If $(SNR)_L$ is large ($+10$ db or more), the linear approximation is valid; that is,

$$\overline{\theta_{no}^2} = \frac{1}{2(SNR)_L} \qquad (3\text{-}17)$$

For small $(SNR)_L$, the approximation fails.

In the general case there has been no solution for phase fluctuation versus $(SNR)_L$. However, for the special case of the first-order loop [loop filter transfer function $F(s) = 1$] Tikhonov [Tik-1, 2] and Viterbi [Vit-2, 5] have devised an exact solution of the problem. The asymptotes of $\overline{\theta_{no}^2}$ of the solution reduce to the linear case for large SNR and to $\pi^2/3$ for small SNR. The value of $\pi^2/3$ arises because a random noise with phase uniformly distributed in the range of $-\pi$ to $+\pi$ can be shown to have a mean-square phase of $\pi^2/3$ radians (rms phase fluctuation $\approx 104°$).

The results for the first-order loop are instructive, but not many first-order loops are encountered in practice. An exact analysis has yet to be discovered for the much-used second-order loop. It is, in fact, doubtful that a closed-form solution exists. Nonetheless, several investigators have made reasonable-seeming approximations and have obtained results for the second-order loop, results that are superior to those obtained with a linear assumption.

Van Trees [Van-2] makes use of a branch of nonlinear mathematics known as "Volterra functionals" and obtains a power-series description of the phase variance. Lindsey [Lin-4] extends Viterbi's methods with some approximations of the form of the phase-error statistics and obtains a complicated analytic expression for the variance. Tausworthe [Tau-1] borrows one feature of Viterbi's analysis (as discussed later) and arrives at expressions relating damping and threshold, as well as variance, to the SNR. All analyses reduce to the results of the linear approximation (3-15) for large enough $(SNR)_L$; those of Lindsey and Tausworthe approach a phase variance of $\pi^2/3$ as $(SNR)_L$ approaches zero.

Viterbi's method, leading to a limiting variance of $\pi^2/3$ is disturbing to the intuition since experience would seem to indicate that jitter should increase at least in proportion to increasing noise. However, his definition of phase sheds some light on the meaning of the asymptotic phase $\pi^2/3$. He considers phase modulo 2π; that is, if actual phase is ψ, he considers instead a phase of $\phi = \psi - 2n\pi$, where n is an integer such that $-\pi \leq \phi \leq +\pi$. To take account of the fact that ψ can exceed $\pm\pi$ radians he obtains the probability of skipping cycles. Thus, although $\overline{\theta_{no}^2}$ approaches $\pi^2/3$ (modulo 2π), the loop is continually slipping cycles.

The reason for this unusual definition of phase lies in the unfortunate mathematical properties of θ_{no}. Because there is some finite, if very small, probability of skipping cycles if any (gaussian) noise at all is present, an infinite number of cycles will have been skipped after an infinite time. Therefore, because the averaging interval for determining mean-square jitter must be infinite to be mathematically correct, the rigorous application of the conventional definition of phase jitter leads to an infinite answer.*

Viterbi's redefinition of phase (modulo 2π) avoids the mathematical difficulty. Furthermore, hardly any laboratory phase meter will have a range of more than 2π radians; its measurements will be modulo 2π, and determination of larger variations must be made by counting skipped cycles.

From these considerations it appears that phase jitter is not a good criterion of threshold and that some other quantity may be preferable; for example, the probability of skipping cycles. Viterbi [Vit-5] has computed this quantity for the first-order loop, and although no exact solution exists for the second-order loop Sanneman and Rowbotham [San-1] have performed a computer simulation and obtained approximate results. They considered a high-gain loop with damping of 0.707 and obtained the average elapsed time to skip one cycle for various noise conditions. The investigation included several initial conditions, but the result for zero initial error is sufficiently representative and is the only case presented here.†

Sanneman and Rowbotham's results are shown in Figure 3-2. The straight-line fit to the data on semilog paper suggests that mean time to unlock may be represented by

$$T_{av} = \frac{2}{\omega_n} \exp\left[\pi(\text{SNR})_L\right] \qquad (3\text{-}18)$$

at least for the range of SNR covered in Figure 3-2. This equation seems acceptable inasmuch as Viterbi [Vit-5] in his exact analysis of the first-order loop also arrives at a simple exponential approximation at sufficiently high SNR. It would be of considerable interest to know whether (3-18) is valid at large SNR also.

For numerical examples, if $B_L = 20$ cps ($\omega_n = 37.7$ rad/sec) and $(\text{SNR})_L = 1$, then $T_{av} \approx 1.2$ sec, and performance is very poor. If, instead, $(\text{SNR})_L = 10$, then [assuming that (3-18) is valid for large SNR] $T_{av} \approx 4.4 \times 10^{12}$ sec or about 130,000 years.

Sanneman and Rowbotham obtained their results by many independent

* An alternative point of view can be produced by recognizing that the loop phase jitter—like the random walk—is not a stationary process. The conventional statistics of stationary processes therefore are not directly applicable.

† As might be expected, any phase error (due, for example, to modulation) increases the probability of skipping cycles.

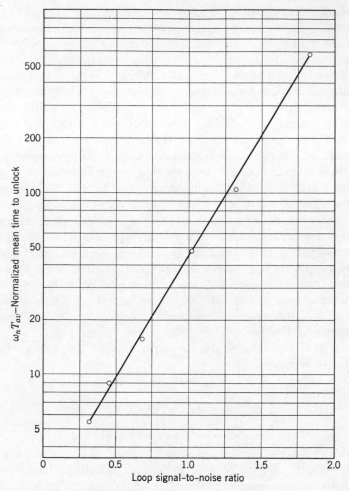

Figure 3-2   Unlock behavior of high-gain, second-order loop, $\zeta = 0.707$.
Datum points ($\bigcirc$) from Sanneman and Rowbotham.

trials on the computer and were able to observe the statistical behavior
of the experiment. They found than an exponential of the form

$$P(T) = 1 - e^{-T/T_{av}}$$

provided a good empirical fit to their data. The quantity $P(T)$ is the
probability that the loop has skipped a cycle (unlocked) after time T has
elapsed, starting from a zero-error initial condition.

   It should be pointed out that these results are obtained only for a
special case, that is, a second-order, constant-bandwidth, high-gain loop

with damping of 0.707. Although intuition may suggest that the results can be applied to other situations, caution should be exercised. In particular, if a limiter is used in the loop, damping and bandwidth are not constant but are functions of the input signal-to-noise ratio (effects of limiters are considered further in Chapter 5).

Furthermore, these results give no indication of loop behavior after the first skipped cycle. We are not told whether the loop settles down (temporarily, of course) in its new phase or whether it falls completely out of lock and proceeds to skip cycles at an ever-increasing rate. There is probably no simple answer to this question; at high SNR one would expect occasional skipping of individual cycles, whereas the catastrophic behavior is more likely to be found at low SNR.

All of these conditions and restrictions notwithstanding, the meaning of Figure 3-2 is clear; loop performance is poor at unity signal-to-noise ratio in the loop and improves rapidly as SNR increases. If an approximate definition of threshold is desired, $(SNR)_L = 1.0$ (i.e., 0 db) will do very well as a lower limit.

The foregoing discussion concerns the common second-order loop; there is almost no quantitative information available on threshold performance of a third-order loop. However, one would not expect it to be very different from the second-order loop.

Chapter Four

Tracking and acquisition

4-1 Linear Tracking

To study tracking we examine the phase error θ_e that results from a specified input, θ_i. A small phase error is usually desired and is considered to be the criterion of good tracking performance.* Phase error is studied because there is no average frequency error in a locked loop. For each cycle of the input there must be a corresponding cycle of the output. If the VCO skips cycles, the loop is considered to have lost lock, even if only momentarily. The problems of unlock behavior are considered in a later section. Here, the concern is with tracking in a locked loop.

Phase error (in the frequency domain) is given by (2-7) as

$$\theta_e(s) = \frac{s\theta_i(s)}{s + K_o K_d F(s)} \tag{4-1}$$

The simplest to analyze are the steady-state errors remaining after any transients have died away. These errors are readily evaluated by means of the final value theorem of Laplace transforms which states

$$\lim_{t \to \infty} y(t) = \lim_{s \to 0} s\, Y(s) \tag{4-2}$$

That is to say, the steady-state value of a function in the time domain is readily determined from inspection of its transform in the frequency domain.

Application of the final value theorem to the phase-error equation yields

$$\lim_{t \to \infty} \theta_e(t) = \lim_{s \to 0} \frac{s^2\, \theta_i(s)}{s + K_o K_d F(s)} \tag{4-3}$$

---

* Discriminators are a special case in which the phase error is the useful output, and therefore close tracking is not necessarily useful.

As a first example, consider the steady-state error resulting from a step change of input phase of magnitude $\Delta\theta$. The Laplace transform of the input is therefore $\theta_i(s) = \Delta\theta/s$ which may be substituted into 4-3 to give

$$\lim_{t \to \infty} \theta_e(t) = \lim_{s \to 0} \frac{s\,\Delta\theta}{s + K_o K_d F(s)} = 0$$

In other words, the loop will eventually track out any change of input phase; there is no steady-state error resulting from a step change of phase.*

For another example, examine the steady-state error resulting from a step change of frequency of magnitude $\Delta\omega$. Input phase is a ramp, and therefore $\theta_i(s) = \Delta\omega/s^2$. Substitution of this value of θ_i into (4-3) results in

$$\lim_{t \to \infty} \theta_e(t) = \lim_{s \to 0} \frac{\Delta\omega}{s + K_o K_d F(s)} = \frac{\Delta\omega}{K_o K_d F(0)} \qquad (4\text{-}4)$$

The product $K_o K_d F(0)$ is often called the "velocity constant" or "d-c loop gain" and is denoted by the symbol K_v. Those familiar with servos will recognize it as the velocity-error coefficient. Note that K_v has the dimensions of frequency.

It is not to be expected that the incoming signal frequency will agree exactly with the free-running (zero control voltage) frequency of the VCO. As a rule, there will be a frequency difference $\Delta\omega$ between the two. The frequency difference may be due to an actual difference between the transmitter and receiver or it may be due to a Doppler shift. In either case the resulting phase error is often called the "velocity error" or simply "static phase error" and is given by

$$\boxed{\theta_v = \frac{\Delta\omega}{K_v}} \qquad (4\text{-}4a)$$

Let us now evaluate K_v for the second-order loop. Two types of loop filter were considered in Chapter 2: a passive filter and an active filter. For the passive filter $F(0) = 1$, whereas for the active filter $F(0) = A$, where A is the d-c gain of an operational amplifier. Assuming that $K_o K_d$ is the same in both cases, we see that K_v will be much larger and θ_v much smaller if an active filter is used. (Voltage gains of 10^2 to 10^7 are typical.) As a practical matter, it is not difficult, in most cases, to make A large enough that θ_v is no more than a few degrees for the maximum frequency displacement encountered. In other words, the phase slope of a phaselock

* Provided that $F(0) \neq 0$.

loop can be made indefinitely small; this feature is of great importance for precision tracking of signals in which phase carries information.

Next, let us suppose that the input frequency is linearly changing with time at a rate of $\Delta\dot{\omega}$ radians per second[2]. Such input behavior might arise from accelerated motion between transmitter and receiver, from change of Doppler frequency during an overhead pass of a satellite, or from sweep-frequency modulation.

Input phase is $\theta_i(s) = \Delta\dot{\omega}/s^3$, and it can be shown that phase error will grow without bound if K_v is finite; it is interesting to calculate this rate of growth. By the final value theorem the steady-state rate of change of phase would be

$$\lim_{t \to \infty} \frac{d\theta_e(t)}{dt} = \lim_{s \to 0} s[s\theta_e(s)]$$

$$= \lim_{s \to 0} \frac{s^3\,\theta_i(s)}{s + K_oK_d\,F(s)} = \lim_{s \to 0} \frac{\Delta\dot{\omega}}{s + K_oK_d\,F(s)}$$

$$= \frac{\Delta\dot{\omega}}{K_v} \text{ radians/sec} \tag{4-5}$$

and the accumulated phase error after an elapsed time t is $\Delta\dot{\omega}t/K_v$. This expression will be recognized as nothing more than the previously derived velocity error and can be neglected for sufficiently large K_v.

Suppose that the gain of the operational amplifier is infinite and that phase error in a second-order loop may be written

$$\theta_e(s) = \frac{s^2\,\theta_i(s)}{s^2 + 2\zeta\omega_n s + \omega_n{}^2} \tag{4-6}$$

This leads to the "acceleration error" (sometimes called "dynamic tracking error").

$$\theta_a = \lim_{t \to \infty} \theta_e(t) = \lim_{s \to 0} \frac{\Delta\dot{\omega}}{s^2 + 2\zeta\omega_n s + \omega_n{}^2} \tag{4-7}$$

$$\boxed{\theta_a = \frac{\Delta\dot{\omega}}{\omega_n{}^2} \text{ radians}} \tag{4-7a}$$

It is sometimes necessary to track an accelerating transmitter without steady-state tracking error. Let us determine the form of $F(s)$ needed to reduce θ_a to zero.

The expression for final value acceleration error is

$$\theta_a = \lim_{s \to 0} \frac{\Delta\dot{\omega}}{s[s + K_oK_dF(s)]} \tag{4-8}$$

In order for θ_a to be zero, it is necessary that $F(s)$ have the form $G(s)/s^2$, where $G(0) \neq 0$. The factor $1/s^2$ implies that the loop filter must contain two cascaded integrators. Closed-loop response then has a polynomial of third degree in its denominator, and the loop is of third-order. Because of this property of eliminating the steady-state acceleration error, a third-order loop is sometimes very useful in tracking satellites and missiles.

Next, let us investigate loop behavior in the presence of a modulated input. For sinusoidal phase modulation

$$\theta_i(t) = \Delta\theta \sin \omega_m t \tag{4-9}$$

and for sinusoidal frequency modulation

$$\theta_i(t) = \frac{\Delta\omega}{\omega_m} \cos \omega_m t \tag{4-10}$$

where $\Delta\theta$ is peak phase deviation, $\Delta\omega$ is peak frequency deviation, and ω_m is modulating frequency.

Phase error may be calculated simply as the steady-state frequency response of (2-7). For phase modulation

$$\theta_e(t) = M \, \Delta\theta \sin (\omega_m t + \phi) \tag{4-11}$$

whereas for frequency modulation

$$\theta_e(t) = M \frac{\Delta\omega}{\omega_m} \cos (\omega_m t + \phi) \tag{4-12}$$

where M is the magnitude of the response and ϕ is the phase shift. In a second-order loop (2-12)

$$M = \omega_m \left[\frac{\omega_m^2 + \omega_n^4/(K_o K_d)^2}{(\omega_n^2 - \omega_m^2)^2 + (2\zeta\omega_n\omega_m)^2} \right]^{\frac{1}{2}} \tag{4-13}$$

and

$$\phi = \frac{\pi}{2} + \tan^{-1} \frac{\omega_m K_o K_d}{\omega_n^2} - \tan^{-1} \frac{2\zeta\omega_n\omega_m}{\omega_n^2 - \omega_m^2} \tag{4-14}$$

If the second-order loop has high gain (2-11), the response parameters reduce to

$$M = \frac{\omega_m^2}{[(\omega_n^2 - \omega_m^2)^2 + (2\zeta\omega_n\omega_m)^2]^{\frac{1}{2}}} \tag{4-15}$$

and

$$\phi = \pi - \tan^{-1} \frac{2\zeta\omega_n\omega_m}{\omega_n^2 - \omega_m^2} \tag{4-16}$$

For PM with a fixed phase deviation $\Delta\theta$ the phase error is small for low modulating frequencies, rises at 12 db per octave, and eventually levels out at high frequencies to be equal to the deviation. This behavior is the "error response" plotted in Figure 2-4.

For FM with fixed deviation $\Delta\omega$ the phase error is small at low modulation frequencies, rises to a maximum at $\omega_m = \omega_n$, and falls off at higher frequencies. Asymptotes at low and high frequencies are 6 db per octave. Peak error is plotted in Figure 4-1 for several values of damping factor.

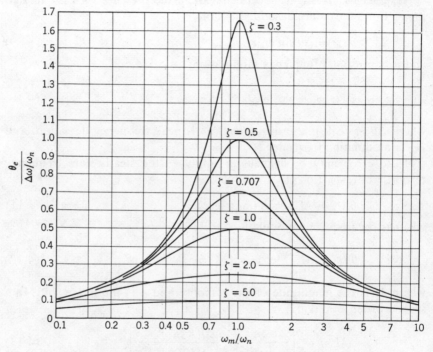

Figure 4-1   Steady-state peak phase error due to sinusoidal FM.
(High-gain, second-order loop.)
By permission of L. A. Hoffman.

Finally, let us consider the transient behavior of loop error for various inputs consisting of the following:

1. A step of phase, $\Delta\theta$ radians.
2. A step of frequency (phase ramp), $\Delta\omega$ radians per second.
3. A step of acceleration (frequency ramp), $\Delta\dot{\omega}$ radians per second^2.

For these inputs, the $\mathcal{L}$-transformed input phase is $\Delta\theta/s$, $\Delta\omega/s^2$, and $\Delta\dot{\omega}/s^3$, respectively. To compute phase errors each input is substituted into (2-7) and inverse $\mathcal{L}$-transforms are then computed (or looked up in tables) to determine time response. The results for the special but important case of a high-gain, second-order loop (2-11) are shown in Table 4-1 [Hof-1].

Table 4-1 Transient Phase Error of Second-Order Loop, $\theta_e(t)$ in Radians (high loop gain; $K_o K_d \gg \omega_n$)

	Phase Step ($\Delta\theta$ radians)	Frequency Step ($\Delta\omega$ rad/sec)	Frequency Ramp ($\Delta\dot\omega$ rad/sec^2)
$\zeta < 1$	$\Delta\theta\left(\cos\sqrt{1-\zeta^2}\,\omega_n t\right.$ $\left.-\dfrac{\zeta}{\sqrt{1-\zeta^2}}\sin\sqrt{1-\zeta^2}\,\omega_n t\right)e^{-\zeta\omega_n t}$	$\dfrac{\Delta\omega}{\omega_n}\left(\dfrac{1}{\sqrt{1-\zeta^2}}\sin\sqrt{1-\zeta^2}\,\omega_n t\right)e^{-\zeta\omega_n t}$	$\dfrac{\Delta\dot\omega t}{K_v}+\dfrac{\Delta\dot\omega}{\omega_n^2}-\dfrac{\Delta\dot\omega}{\omega_n^2}\left(\cos\sqrt{1-\zeta^2}\,\omega_n t\right.$ $\left.+\dfrac{\zeta}{\sqrt{1-\zeta^2}}\sin\sqrt{1-\zeta^2}\,\omega_n t\right)e^{-\zeta\omega_n t}$
$\zeta = 1$	$\Delta\theta(1-\omega_n t)e^{-\omega_n t}$	$\dfrac{\Delta\omega}{\omega_n}(\omega_n t)e^{-\omega_n t}$	$\dfrac{\Delta\dot\omega t}{K_v}+\dfrac{\Delta\dot\omega}{\omega_n^2}-\dfrac{\Delta\dot\omega}{\omega_n^2}(1+\omega_n t)e^{-\omega_n t}$
$\zeta > 1$	$\Delta\theta\left(\cosh\sqrt{\zeta^2-1}\,\omega_n t\right.$ $\left.-\dfrac{\zeta}{\sqrt{\zeta^2-1}}\sinh\sqrt{\zeta^2-1}\,\omega_n t\right)e^{-\zeta\omega_n t}$	$\dfrac{\Delta\omega}{\omega_n}\left(\dfrac{1}{\sqrt{\zeta^2-1}}\sinh\sqrt{\zeta^2-1}\,\omega_n t\right)e^{-\zeta\omega_n t}$	$\dfrac{\Delta\dot\omega t}{K_v}+\dfrac{\Delta\dot\omega}{\omega_n^2}-\dfrac{\Delta\dot\omega}{\omega_n^2}\left(\cosh\sqrt{\zeta^2-1}\,\omega_n t\right.$ $\left.+\dfrac{\zeta}{\sqrt{\zeta^2-1}}\sinh\sqrt{\zeta^2-1}\,\omega_n t\right)e^{-\zeta\omega_n t}$
	Steady-state error = 0	Steady-state error $=\dfrac{\Delta\omega}{K_v}$ (not included above)	Steady state error $=\dfrac{\Delta\dot\omega t}{K_v}+\dfrac{\Delta\dot\omega}{\omega_n^2}$ (included above)

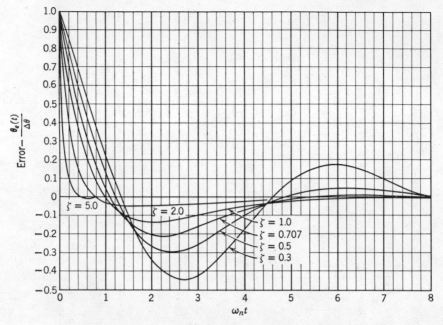

Figure 4-2   Phase error $\theta_e(t)$ due to a step in phase $\Delta\theta$.
By permission of L. A. Hoffman.

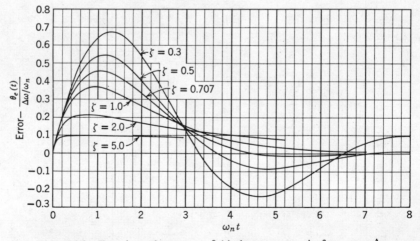

Figure 4-3   Transient phase error $\theta_e(t)$ due to a step in frequency $\Delta\omega$.
(Steady-state velocity error, $\Delta\omega/K_v$, neglected.)
By permission of L. A. Hoffman.

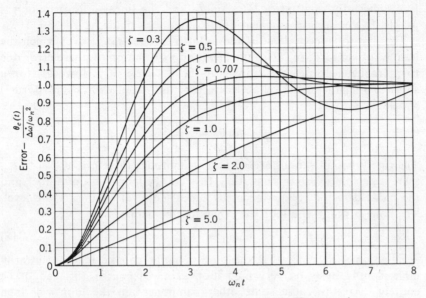

Figure 4-4   Transient phase error $\theta_e(t)$ due to a ramp in frequency $\Delta\dot\omega$.
(Steady-state acceleration error, $\Delta\dot\omega/\omega_n{}^2$, included. Velocity error, $\Delta\dot\omega t/K_v$, neglected.)
By permission of L. A. Hoffman.

These expressions are not unduly complex but are nonetheless quite
tedious to evaluate without a computer. The chore of computation has
already been performed by Hoffman [Hof-1] whose plots of transient
error versus time are shown in Figures 4-2, 4-3, and 4-4 for various
damping factors ζ.

4-2   Hold-In Performance

All of the preceding material on tracking and phase error is based on the
assumption that the error is sufficiently small, thus allowing the loop to be
considered linear in its operation. This assumption becomes progressively
worse as error increases until finally the loop drops out of lock, and the
assumption becomes worthless. In this section the linear assumption is
discarded, and the limiting conditions for which a loop holds lock are
investigated.

The most commonly encountered phase detector* is one whose output
voltage e_d is related to phase error by

$$e_d = K_d \sin \theta_e \tag{4-17}$$

* For discussion of various types of phase detectors, see Chapter 5.

For sufficiently small error $\theta_e \approx \sin \theta_e$, and the linear approximation is usable. In this section no linear approximation is made.

The first topic considered is the input frequency range over which the loop will hold lock. In (4-4a) the linear approximation of phase error due to a frequency offset was shown to be $\theta_v = \Delta\omega/K_v$. However, for a sinusoidal-characteristic phase detector the true expression [Gru-1] should be

$$\sin \theta_v = \frac{\Delta\omega}{K_v}$$

The sine function cannot exceed unit magnitude; therefore, if $\Delta\omega > K_v$, there is no solution to this equation. Instead, the loop falls out of lock and the phase-detector voltage becomes a beat-note rather then a d-c level. The hold-in range of a loop may therefore be defined as

$$\Delta\omega_{\mathrm{H}} = \pm K_v \tag{4-18}$$

Equation 4-18 states that the hold-in range can be made arbitrarily large, simply by using very high loop gain. Of course, this cannot be entirely correct because some other component in the loop will then saturate before the phase detector; that is to say, to achieve any given frequency deviation of the VCO some definite control voltage is needed. However, the loop amplifier (if one is used) has some maximum voltage it can deliver and the VCO has some maximum voltage it can accept. If either of these limits is exceeded, the loop unlocks. It is not uncommon to find active loops with such high gain that the amplifier will saturate when static phase error is only a few degrees.

Dynamic error in a second-order loop was previously (4-7a) approximated as $\theta_a = \Delta\dot{\omega}/\omega_n^2$. The correct expression for a phase detector with a sinusoidal characteristic should be

$$\sin \theta_a = \frac{\Delta\dot{\omega}}{\omega_n^2} \tag{4-19}$$

from which it may be deduced that the maximum permissible rate of change of input frequency is [Vit-1]

$$\Delta\dot{\omega} = \omega_n^2 \tag{4-20}$$

If the input rate should exceed this amount the loop will fall out of lock. (To anticipate matters covered in the next section, acquisition of lock at sweep rates approaching ω_n^2 is either very difficult or impossible.)

For a step of frequency Figure 4-3 shows that the transient phase error greatly exceeds the static error. One might well ask, can the transient error pull the loop out of lock, even if the static error is within the hold-in range? The answer is not simple; it depends on circumstances and is perhaps not yet fully established in the literature. A summary of published results is presented in the following paragraphs.

First, consider the infinite-gain, second-order loop. Rue and Lux [Rue-1] point out that, in principle, this type of loop can never lose lock permanently. If a large frequency step is applied, the loop unlocks, skips cycles for a while, and then locks up once again. The phase error is a ringing oscillation for a number of cycles corresponding to the number of cycles skipped.

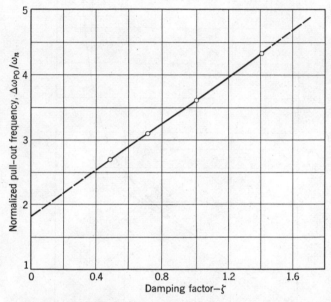

Figure 4-5   Pull-out frequency of high-gain second-order loop. Datum points from Viterbi [Vit-1].

There is some frequency-step limit below which the loop does not skip cycles but remains in lock; we denote this limit as the "pull-out frequency". Viterbi [Vit-1] has performed analog computer simulation of the behavior of loops of various types and parameters. From his report we may determine the pull-out frequency of a second-order loop, the results of which are plotted against damping factor in Figure 4-5. The data are well fitted by a straight line with the equation

$$\Delta\omega_{\mathrm{PO}} = 1.8\omega_n(\zeta + 1) \tag{4-21}$$

at least for the range of ζ covered by Viterbi.

To reiterate, if a step of frequency is less than $\Delta\omega_{\mathrm{PO}}$ the transient error is such that the loop remains in lock. If $\Delta\omega > \Delta\omega_{PO}$, the loop skips cycles before settling into lock once again.

For $\Delta\omega = \Delta\omega_{PO}$, the peak phase error is 180 degrees not 90, as might be supposed. However, the error increases rapidly as soon as it exceeds 90 degrees and therefore the frequency step causing 90 degrees peak error

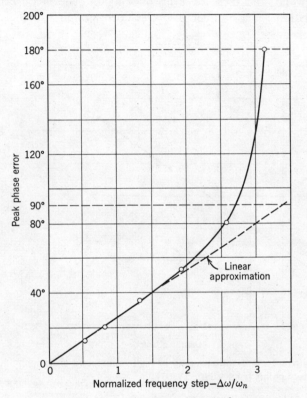

Figure 4-6   Peak phase error due to frequency step.
High-gain, second-order loop; $\zeta = 0.707$.
Datum points from Viterbi [Vit-1].

is only slightly less than $\Delta\omega_{PO}$. Figure 4-6 illustrates the situation for the special case of $\zeta = 0.707$.

This discussion of pull-out frequency and peak error (below pull-out) has been restricted to the high-gain second-order loop. Other-order loops [Rey-1, Vit-1] have very different performance. For example, the first-order loop (no loop filter) has a hold-in frequency equal to its 3-db frequency, which is also equal to its pull-out frequency and, as discussed later, to its pull-in frequency; that is,

$$\Delta\omega = K_v \qquad\qquad (4-22)$$

where $\Delta\omega$ has the meaning of any of the foregoing frequencies and K_v is the loop gain. Maximum possible phase error cannot exceed 90 degrees.

For a second-order loop of moderate gain we would expect performance to be degraded from the high-gain case. It is also to be expected that the pull-out frequency, as already defined, would probably be reduced, but no quantitative determination of the reduction has been made. Furthermore, if the step is sufficiently large, the loop will drop out of lock and stay out. Let us call this limit the "dropout" frequency. (It is more commonly [Rey-1] called the pull-out frequency, but that name has already been used here for another quantity. Available terminology is becoming scarce.)

It should be clear that the dropout frequency $\Delta\omega_{DO} < K_v$. There are indications [Rey-1] that $0.72\ K_v < \Delta\omega_{DO} < K_v$, but this is not at all certain. Intuitively, it would seem that the drop-out frequency might equal the pull-in frequency (which is discussed in the next section); this topic bears further investigation.

Third-order loops are discussed by Viterbi [Vit-1] and Gupta [Gup-1]. Briefly, the third-order loop exhibits great improvement in tracking performance over a second-order loop when the input is a frequency ramp. For the particular third-order loop described previously (coincident open-loop zeros, critical damping of closed-loop poles) the peak error due to a frequency step is almost identical to the value occurring in a second-order loop with equal noise bandwidth and $\zeta = 0.707$.

We must also be concerned with loop hold-in problems when the input signal is angle-modulated (e.g., phaselock used as a discriminator in FM-FM telemetry). Following Martin [Mar-3], we distinguish between "carrier-tracking loops" in which the modulation is entirely outside the loop bandwidth and "modulation-tracking loops" in which the modulation spectrum is primarily within the loop bandwidth. The first type of loop is used for PM demodulation, whereas the second is used as an FM discriminator.

In the carrier-tracking loop the modulation must be restricted so that there actually is a carrier to track. If sinusoidal phase modulation of peak deviation θ is applied, the carrier strength is proportional to the zero-order Bessel function $J_o(\theta)$. This function passes through its first zero for $\theta = 2.4$ radians (137 degrees). Moreover, to avoid severe distortion of the recovered modulation the deviation has to be less than 90 degrees. In other words, when a carrier-tracking phaselock loop is used as a PM demodulator, the modulation index must be limited to relatively small values (certainly less than 2.4).

The situation for FM is not so restrictive. Because the loop tracks the modulation, it is possible to have an arbitrarily large modulation index. It is only nceessary that the loop bandwidth be wide enough to track the modulation sufficiently closely. Runyan [Run-1] defines "sufficiently closely" as meaning that the loop phase error remains within the linear range of the phase detector. This restraint will avoid distortion, but it is conservative with respect to hold-in capabilities.

The curves of Figure 4-1 show peak sinusoidal phase error versus modulating frequency for fixed frequency deviation. It is apparent that the greatest error occurs when the modulating frequency is equal to the loop natural frequency. As a reasonable rule of thumb, the loop should remain locked if this peak error always remains less than 90 degrees.

In all of these discussions of hold-in and pull-out behavior, it has been tacitly assumed that the loop was essentially noise-free. If noise is present it can be expected that performance will be degraded. Where quantitative results have been given, a sinusoidal-characteristic phase detector has been assumed. If a triangular or saw-toothed characteristic (see Chapter 5) were used instead, it is likely that improved hold-in performance could be obtained. Finally, the phase detector has been assumed to be the only nonlinear element in the loop. The analyses might have to be revised drastically if saturation of the loop amplifier or VCO were a significant problem.

4-3   Acquisition

For all the topics discussed so far in this and preceding chapters it has been tacitly assumed that the loop was initially in lock. The purpose of this section is to examine an out-of-lock loop and explain how it may be brought into lock.

There are a number of methods by which lock can be acquired:

1. If, for some reason, the frequency difference between input and VCO is less than the loop bandwidth, the loop will lock up almost instantaneously without slipping cycles. The maximum frequency difference for which this fast acquisition is possible is called the lock-in frequency $\Delta\omega_L$.

2. There are loop types (including the most common second-order loop) in which the VCO frequency will slowly walk in toward the input frequency, despite the fact that the initial difference frequency may greatly exceed the loop bandwidth. The maximum difference frequency from which the loop will eventually lock itself is called the pull-in frequency $\Delta\omega_P$.

3. The loop could be outside pull-in range, or pull-in might require too long a time, in which case the VCO can be swept at a suitable rate in order to search for the signal.

4. Provided that noise level is sufficiently low, faster acquisition is possible if the loop bandwidth is widened.

5. A frequency discriminator can be used to adjust the VCO to within lock-in range of the input frequency in order to acquire rapidly.

The remainder of this chapter is devoted to consideration of all of these topics.

First-Order Loop

It is instructive to begin the discussion with an analysis of a first-order loop. Because there is no filter in this loop [$F(s) = 1$], the linearized loop transfer function is

$$H(s) = \frac{K_v}{s + K_v} \tag{4-23}$$

The 3-db frequency (loop bandwidth) is K_v radians per second, and it was shown earlier (eq. 4-18) that the hold-in frequency limit is also K_v.

To show lock-in performance, we derive the nonlinear differential equation of the loop and analyze its meaning. For this purpose let ω_i be the input frequency (assumed constant) and let ω_o be equal to the center frequency of the VCO so that the instantaneous frequency of the VCO is $\omega_o + K_o e_d$. Voltage $e_d = K_d \sin \theta$ is the error voltage out of the phase detector.

Input phase is $\omega_i t$ and output phase is

$$\theta_o = \omega_o t + \int_o^t K_o e_d \, dt$$

$$= \omega_o t + \int_o^t K_o K_d \sin \theta_e \, dt \tag{4-24}$$

Phase error is

$$\theta_e = \theta_i - \theta_o = \omega_i t - \omega_o t - \int_o^t K_v \sin \theta_e \, dt \tag{4-25}$$

Let $\omega_i - \omega_o = \Delta \omega$ and differentiate to obtain

$$\dot{\theta}_e = \Delta \omega - K_v \sin \theta_e \tag{4-26}$$

This is the nonlinear differential equation of the first-order phaselock loop. The loop is locked only if $\dot{\theta}_e$ is zero, by definition of lock. However, we must show that the converse is true; that if $\dot{\theta}_e = 0$ the loop is necessarily locked.

From the first condition the hold-in limit is obtained; that is, if $\dot{\theta}_e = 0$, then $\sin \theta_e = \Delta \omega / K_v$. Because $\sin \theta_e$ cannot exceed unity, the loop can lock only if $\Delta \omega / K_v < 1$.

To examine the second question it is useful to divide (4-26) through by K_v and then plot $\dot{\theta}_e / K_v$ versus θ_e, as in Figure 4-7.* From the figure it may be seen that, if $|\Delta \omega / K_v| < 1$, there are two points (nulls) in each interval

* This analysis follows a similar one by Viterbi [Vit-1]. Figure 4-7 is the "phase plane plot."

of 2π for which $\dot{\theta}_e$ goes to zero. At a null the phase difference between input and VCO is a constant and therefore the loop must be locked, by definition.

Adjacent nulls are of opposite slope. To analyze the behavior of the loop, suppose that the operating point is slightly displaced from one of the nulls. For one of negative slope the sign of $\dot{\theta}_e$ drives θ_e toward the null. (As an example, if phase displacement is slightly negative from a negative-

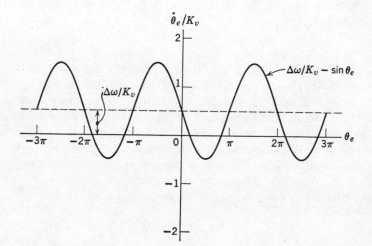

Figure 4-7   Phase plane plot of first-order loop ($\Delta\omega/K_v = \frac{1}{2}$).

slope null, the sign of $\dot{\theta}_e$ is positive and θ_e must necessarily increase—in the direction toward the null.) Conversely, a displacement from one of the positive-slope nulls will drive the state of the loop away from the null. Thus the negative-slope nulls are stable, the positive-slope nulls are unstable.

Prior to lock $\dot{\theta}_e$ is nonzero, which means that θ_e must change (increase or decrease) monotonically. For this reason θ_e must eventually take on the value of one of the stable nulls (provided, of course, that $\Delta\omega < K_v$). When θ_e reaches a stable null, the loop is locked and θ_e remains fixed at the static error. From this argument, it may be concluded that the lock-in and pull-out frequencies are both equal to K_v radians per second in the first-order loop.

Because every cycle has a stable null, θ_e cannot change by more than a half cycle before locking. Thus there is no cycle-skipping in the lock-up process. The time required to lock up depends on the initial values of phase and frequency, but, as a rough rule of thumb, it will be on the order of $1/K_v$ seconds.

Second-Order Loop; Lock-In

Because a first-order loop is so rarely found in practice, its analysis is of interest only for the light it sheds on higher-order loops. In particular, a second-order loop is of greatest concern because of its widespread use. We first obtain an expression for lock-in frequency and then discuss the pull-in phenomenon.

The frequency response of the loop filter of a second-order loop is shown in Figure 4-8. At high frequencies the gain of the filter is $\tau_2/(\tau_1 + \tau_2)$ for a passive filter or just τ_2/τ_1 for an active filter. (Note that the

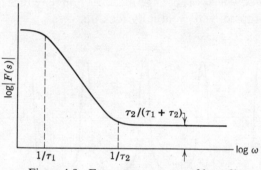

Figure 4-8   Frequency response of loop filter.

gain of the amplifier does not enter into the high-frequency gain.) Total loop gain at high frequencies is therefore $K_o K_d \tau_2/(\tau_1 + \tau_2)$ or $K_o K_d \tau_2/\tau_1$.

At high frequencies this loop is indistinguishable from a first-order loop with the same gain. However, for the first-order loop it was shown that the lock-in frequency was equal to the loop gain. The same should be true for the second-order loop [Ric-2]; the lock-in frequency is equal to the high-frequency loop gain.

$$\Delta\omega_{\mathrm{L}} = \frac{K_o K_d \tau_2}{\tau_1 + \tau_2} \quad \text{(passive filter)}$$

or

$$\Delta\omega_{\mathrm{L}} = \frac{K_o K_d \tau_2}{\tau_1} \quad \text{(active filter)}$$

(4-27)

By making use of (2-10) the lock-in frequency can be expressed in terms of the loop parameters as

$$\boxed{\Delta\omega_L \approx 2\zeta\omega_n} \tag{4-28}$$

In other words, the lock-in performance of the second-order loop is similar to that of the first-order loop. If the signal appears within the loop bandwidth (approximately), the loop locks on immediately without skipping cycles. The lock-up transient occupies a time on the order of $1/\omega_n$ seconds.

Earlier it was shown that the hold-in range of any loop was K_v. In the usual second-order loop K_v is much larger than ω_n so that the hold-in range is much larger than the lock-in range.

Pull-In

There is also a frequency interval called the pull-in range. If the initial frequency difference (between VCO and input) is within the pull-in range, the VCO frequency will slowly change in a direction to reduce the difference and, if not interrupted, will eventually lock up.

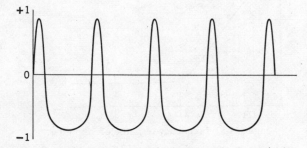

Figure 4-9   Typical beat-note waveshape, first-order loop, $\Delta\omega/K_v = 1.10$.

Pull-in behavior may be understood by recognizing that the phase detector output, in the unlocked condition, consists of a beat-note at the difference frequency between the input and the VCO. The beat-note in a second-order loop is reduced in amplitude by the factor $\tau_2/(\tau_1 + \tau_2)$ by the loop filter, but it is not suppressed completely. As far as the beat-note is concerned, the loop appears to be first-order with reduced gain.

The portion of the beat-note that passes through the filter will frequency-modulate the VCO. Therefore the phase-detector output is the product of a sine wave and a frequency-modulated wave. Since the modulating frequency is equal to the beat frequency, the beat-note could hardly be sinusoidal.

Richman [Ric-2] has derived the waveform of the beat-note for a first-order loop by integrating the differential equation (4-26) of the loop. The explicit equation describing the waveform is cumbersome and does not provide much insight into the problem. However, a plot of the waveform, as in Figure 4-9, is very revealing, and the nonsinusoidal character of the beat-note is evident. Moreover, and vitally important, the positive and negative excursions are obviously unequal in area, and therefore the phase-detector output must contain a d-c component, even before lock is obtained. It is the presence of this component that allows pull-in to occur.

Once the existence of a d-c component is recognized, an alternative explanation of its presence aids understanding; that is, the beat-note, of fundamental frequency $\Delta\omega_i$, frequency-modulates the VCO whose center frequency is ω_o. This modulation generates FM sidebands in the VCO output at frequencies $\omega_k = \omega_o + k\Delta\omega_i$, where k takes on all integral values. In the phase detector this modulated output is multiplied by the sinusoidal input with frequency ω_i.

The difference signal out of the phase detector consists of individual signals at all the frequencies $\omega_i - \omega_k = \omega_i - \omega_o - k\,\Delta\omega_i$. Recall however, that $\Delta\omega_i = \omega_i - \omega_o$ and therefore $\omega_i - \omega_k = \omega_o - k(\omega_i - \omega_o) = (1 - k)\,(\omega_i - \omega_o)$. The individual signal corresponding to $k = 1$ has a frequency of zero; that is, $k = 1$ corresponds to a d-c component.

In a first-order loop the effect is not of much value; if the initial difference frequency exceeds the lock-in frequency the magnitude of the d-c component is insufficient to pull into lock. However, the average difference frequency is reduced; that is, even the first-order loop will tend to pull toward lock, despite the fact that it will not reach lock.

The second-order loop includes an integrator in its loop filter. This integrator builds up an increasing output in response to a d-c input; the accumulated output (delivered to the VCO) can greatly exceed the magnitude of the filtered beat-note that modulates the VCO. As the integrator output builds up, the VCO frequency is adjusted toward the direction of lock. If the initial difference frequency is not too great, the loop will eventually lock up.

A number of authors [Gru-1, Rey-1, Ric-2, Vit-1] have attempted to obtain explicit formulas for the pull-in ranges of a second-order loop. All were forced to make approximations, and, because each has taken a different approach, they all arrive at somewhat different results. The algebraic forms of the individual results (except for Rey's) are fairly similar, and any one of the forms could probably be used to obtain a rough approximation for pull-in frequency.

Fortunately, Gruen has provided experimental data which indicate that Richman's derivation best fits reality, at least for high-gain loops. Richman's formula for pull-in frequency is

$$\Delta\omega_P \approx \sqrt{2}(2\zeta\omega_n K_v - \omega_n^2)^{1/2} \qquad (4\text{-}29)$$

This formula fits Gruen's data very well for moderate to high gain ($\omega_n/K_v < 0.4$) but is very poor for low gain ($\omega_n/K_v > 0.5$). For a high-gain loop (active filter) the equation reduces to

$$\Delta\omega_P = 2\sqrt{\zeta\omega_n K_v} \qquad\qquad (4\text{-}30)$$

To reiterate the meaning of pull-in, if initial frequency difference $|\Delta\omega|$ between input and VCO is less than $\Delta\omega_P$, the loop will eventually pull into lock, unaided (provided it is not disturbed).

Viterbi [Vit-1] and Richman [Ric-2] both derive approximate values for the time required for a loop to pull into lock for some initial frequency offset, $\Delta\omega$. Viterbi's answer is

$$T_P \approx \frac{(\Delta\omega)^2}{2\zeta\omega_n^3} \qquad\qquad (4\text{-}31)$$

Because of the approximations, this formula should not be applied if $\Delta\omega$ is either very large (near $\Delta\omega_P$) or very small (near $\Delta\omega_L$). It is best applied in the midrange and should be considered as the time required to pull in from the initial offset to a beat frequency equal to $\Delta\omega_L$ (at which time, of of course, the loop quickly locks in). For the special case of a high-gain loop with $\zeta = 0.707$, the pull-in time is

$$T_P = \frac{27(\Delta\omega)^2}{256 B_L^3} \approx \frac{4.2(\Delta f)^2}{B_L^3} \sec \qquad\qquad (4\text{-}32)$$

A narrow-band loop can take a very long time to pull in. For example, consider a situation in which $\Delta f = 1$ kHz and $B_L = 10$ Hz. Pull-in time would be one hour and ten minutes, which is intolerably long, even for deep space applications. Moreover, in practical equipment it is entirely likely that offset of the phase detector will exceed the small d-c pull-in voltage to the extent that no pull-in effect will be observed.

Sweep

Because of long pull-in time it is very often necessary to use some other method in order to acquire lock much more rapidly. One expedient commonly used applies a sweep voltage to the VCO and searches for the input frequency. If done properly, the loop will lock up as the VCO frequency sweeps into the input frequency.

From the earlier discussion on the question of hold-in in the presence of a frequency ramp it should be evident that the sweep rate must not be allowed to become excessive. We have already shown that the loop cannot hold lock if the sweep rate $\Delta\dot\omega$ exceeds ω_n^2. If a loop cannot *hold* lock on a signal, it certainly will be unable to *acquire* lock. Therefore an absolute maximum limit on the allowable sweep rate is $\Delta\dot{\omega} < \omega_n^2$ (for a PD with sinusoidal characteristic).

Viterbi has investigated acquisition problems by means of phase-plane trajectories [Vit-1]. He discovered that acquisition is not certain, even if $\Delta\dot{\omega} < \omega_n^2$ and the loop is noise-free. If $\Delta\dot{\omega}$ becomes somewhat larger than $\omega_n^2/2$, there is a possibility that the VCO can sweep right through the input frequency without locking. The chance of locking or nonlocking

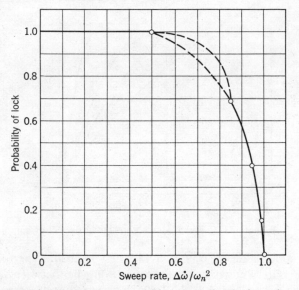

Figure 4-10   Probability of sweep acquisition. Second-order loop; $\zeta = 0.707$; no noise. Datum points from Viterbi [Vit-1].

depends on the random initial conditions of frequency and phase. Viterbi's phase-plane trajectories were used to compute the probability of locking graphically, and it is plotted against sweep rate in Figure 4-10. These results apply directly only to the special case of a high-gain second-order loop with $\zeta = 0.707$. However, qualitatively similar behavior should be expected for other damping factors.

Further qualitative information on sweep acquisition behavior is available from the simulation study by Frazier and Page [Fra-1].* Their paper indicates that for fixed natural frequency and sweep rate the probability of lock is lowered as damping decreases. See Figure 4-11, in which

---

* Although there appears to be an underlying error that makes the interpretation of almost all quantitative results open to question, this paper is useful for providing insight into the qualitative behavior of loops.

it seems implied that the loop should be heavily damped, at least until it is locked.

Such a conclusion is premature; loop-noise bandwidth varies with damping even though natural frequency is fixed (refer to Figure 3-1). On the basis of fixed-noise bandwidth, the largest value of ω_n (and therefore the largest maximum sweep rate) occurs for $\zeta = \frac{1}{2}$. Yet the probability of acquiring lock at sweep rates less than $\omega_n{}^2$ improves as damping increases.

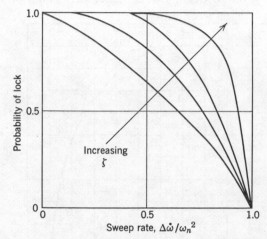

Figure 4-11   Probability of sweep acquisition showing effect of damping.

There will be some value of ζ that provides best acquisition performance; the exact value is not known, but it almost certainly lies between 0.5 and 2.

So far we have assumed that the loop is essentially noise-free. In real life noise is always with us and must be taken into account. Simple intuition leads us to expect that noise will make it more difficult to acquire a signal; it would be useful if this difficulty could be expressed by a number.

Frazier and Page's experiments provide empirical data which suggest that sweep rate should be reduced by a factor of $[1 - (\mathrm{SNR})_L^{-\frac{1}{2}}]$ if an acceptably high probability of acquisition is to be maintained in the presence of noise. This expression predicts that acquisition becomes impossible at 0 db signal-to-noise ratio in the loop.

The result is based on the assumption that loop bandwidth remains constant under all conditions. However, it is common practice to employ limiters in phaselock equipments. When a limiter is used, the gain of the loop—and therefore the damping and bandwidth—are functions of the signal-to-noise ratio at the input to the limiter. The effect is such that the bandwidth becomes narrower as the SNR decreases. (The subject of limiters is covered in Chapter 5.) Therefore, when a limiter is used, the acquisition sweep rate must be considerably reduced from the no-noise condition. Reduction is necessary both because of the presence of noise and because of bandwidth narrowing.

These same facts can be restated in a more optimistic manner. If two phaselock loops are to have the same threshold tracking ability, they must have the same bandwidth under low-signal conditions. A loop containing a limiter will widen its bandwidth as the signal-to-noise ratio improves and thereby will be capable of accommodating much faster sweep rates. If the loop contains no limiter, the bandwidth remains constant at the low-signal value, and any permissible increase of sweep rate is due entirely to the reduction of noise in the loop.

Frazier and Page have obtained an empirical equation which predicts the sweep rate that will provide 90 per cent probability of acquisition, while taking account of noise and the effect of limiting. Their results may be adapted* to

$$\Delta\dot{\omega}_{\max} = \frac{[1 - (\text{SNR})_L^{-\frac{1}{2}}](\alpha/\alpha_0)\omega_{no}^2}{1 + d} \tag{4-33}$$

where α is the signal suppression factor due to the limiter (see Chapter 5), α_o is the signal suppression factor measured at some arbitrary input SNR (usually threshold), ω_{no} is loop natural frequency measured at the same input SNR, and d is a factor depending on damping.

If $\zeta < 1$, $d = \exp(-\zeta\pi/\sqrt{1 - \zeta^2})$, whereas, if $\zeta \geq 1$, $d = 0$. If, for the minimum signal to be tracked, $\zeta = 0.707$ (a very common condition), d will be less than 0.05 for all larger signals and therefore, compared with unity, may be neglected.

Equation 4-33 predicts a maximum allowable sweep rate. For large $(\text{SNR})_L$ the predicted maximum is $\Delta\dot{\omega} = \omega_n^2$, which, of course, is the greatest rate that can be tracked, even in the absence of noise. For this reason, and because the equation is supposed to predict a rate that gives only 90 percent probability of acquisition, it is advisable to sweep at a lower rate in order to provide a margin of safety. When using this equation, it is important to remember that $(\text{SNR})_L$ is not directly proportional to input SNR. Since loop bandwidth changes according to the presence of the limiter, loop signal-to-noise ratio is also a function of α.

So far, acquisition for only first- and second-order loops has been discussed. Very little seems to be known about acquisition behavior of

---

* Actually, their equation is greater than that shown here by a factor of $\sqrt{2}$. It is believed that there is a consistent error of 1.4 to 1.5 in the value of loop gain they used which leads to incorrect numerical interpretation of many of their results.

third-order loops and except for a few cautious statements by Viterbi [Vit-1] nothing appears to have been published on the subject. There is, however, some fear among designers that sweep acquisition with a closed loop may be unstable, and various expedients to avoid such instability are often encountered. One solution is to search for a signal with the loop open and then stop the sweep and close the loop when a signal is detected. Another solution is to search for a signal with a second-order loop and change the loop filter to obtain a third-order loop when the signal has been acquired. It is not at all certain that these "solutions" have a real problem; more investigation is still needed.

All quantitative relations in this chapter are based on an implicit assumption of a phase detector with a sinusoidal characteristic. Other characteristics are examined in Chapter 5; if some other type of phase detector is used, the results that were obtained here will have to be revised accordingly.

4-4   Techniques of Acquisition

Sweep Methods

Frequency sweep is obtained by applying a ramp voltage to the VCO input, which may be derived from an independent sweep generator. However, in a second-order loop a simpler method is available. The loop filter contains an integrator; if a step function is applied to the filter input, the output will contain the desired ramp. Slope of the ramp (and therefore sweep rate) may be controlled by adjusting the magnitude of the input step. One may consider that the VCO is being slewed by the step voltage.

Some portion of the step (approximately τ_2/τ_1) appears directly in the output of the filter and causes a corresponding jump in VCO frequency just as the sweep begins. The particular application must be able to tolerate such a jump. If it cannot, an independent sweep circuit, without a jump, must be used.

Suppose that the sweep voltage (however derived) continued to be applied, even after the loop locked up. If that were to happen, there would be a static phase error of the exact sign and magnitude needed to cancel the sweep voltage, and the VCO would thus be held at the proper frequency. To a first approximation, the sweep voltage could be allowed to continue and simply ignored, for although the phase error it would cause represents a loop disturbance, it might well be of tolerable magnitude. In some cases the sweep voltage might reach so large a value that the filter amplifier or the VCO would be saturated. This eventuality, however, can be avoided simply by not sweeping outside the linear limit of the loop components.

Ordinarily, direction of sweep is periodically reversed as the sweep reaches some predetermined limits.

Now suppose that the loop has been locked for a while and that the signal fades out for a short time. Fading causes unlock, and the sweep immediately carries the VCO frequency off from the signal frequency. When the signal returns, the VCO will have been carried off to some distance and very likely will be receding further. Obviously, presence of the sweep voltage makes reacquisition more difficult than it need be. For this reason, it is good practice to turn off the sweep voltage once lock has been acquired. Turn-off need not be very rapid; the preceding arguments have shown that sweep can often be tolerated during lock. There should be adequate time allowed to verify, with a high degree of certainty, that lock actually has been obtained.

Memory

In the absence of sweep the VCO of a second-order loop will tend to remain close to its locked frequency in the event of a signal dropout. When the signal returns, reacquisition by lock-in or pull-in should be very rapid. Thus the loop has a velocity (frequency) memory. Frequency information is stored in the form of charge in the integrator. When signal drops out, the loop opens and the discharge time constant of the integrator is $|A| R_1 C$. (See Figure 2-2 for nomenclature.) The gain A is unity in a passive loop, and so the memory evaporates fairly quickly. However, in an active loop A can be very large, and one would expect long holding times.

This expectation is only partly met in actual equipment. Any real d-c amplifier will have some offset and drift, and any real phase detector will have some small d-c output (due, for example, to imperfect balance), particularly if there is a noise input. These drifts, unbalances, offsets, and rectified noise all combine to form a small slewing voltage that is integrated and drives the VCO away from its proper frequency. Presumably there is some optimum d-c gain that balances the effects of integrator discharge against those of unwanted slewing and thereby achieves a maximum memory time. Any expedient that reduces offset will permit a higher gain and longer memory.

Another approach is sometimes taken when operator intervention is allowable. In this situation control voltage to the VCO is monitored, and the VCO is manually tuned* to keep the voltage at zero. In this way the correct frequency is represented by zero charge on the integrator, and there can be no evaporation of memory. The offset problem is handled by adjusting the amplifier d-c gain so that amplified offset, after the integrator

---

* Mechanical servos have also been used.

has reached its final value, is small enough to maintain the VCO within easy pull-in range of the signal frequency.

Memory capability of other loop types is of some interest. A first-order loop can have no memory; if the signal fades out, the VCO immediately reverts to its center value. On the other hand, because of its two integrators, a third-order loop has an acceleration memory; if an accelerating signal— such as the Doppler signal from a satellite—should fade out, the loop will keep tracking at the same rate of change of frequency. This feature is particularly attractive in a tumbling satellite that exhibits periodic and frequent fading.

Lock Indication

Closely associated with the subject of acquisition is the question of how to tell whether the loop is in lock. If loop signal-to-noise ratio is moderately

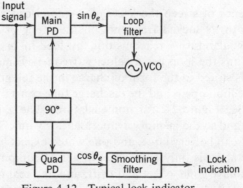

Figure 4-12   Typical lock indicator.

good and the input signal does not jump around too much, it is not too difficult to detect lock. However, near threshold conditions lock may not be easy to detect, and, in fact, the very definition of lock may become hazy (as discussed in Chapter 3).

Even if the signal is good, the locked condition cannot be detected instantaneously. Instead, it is necessary to filter the indication for some appropriate length of time (generally comparable to inverse loop bandwidth) to reduce the confusion caused by noise. For this reason there must necessarily be some delay between the time a loop locks up and the time that lock is positively indicated.

A method of lock indication employed almost universally is the "quadrature" or "auxiliary" phase detector. A typical arrangement is shown in Figure 4-12. The quadrature phase detector has the received signal applied as one input and a 90 degree, phase-shifted version of the

VCO as the other. The main phase detector has an output voltage proportional to sin θ_e, whereas the quadrature output is proportional to cos θ_e. In the locked condition θ_e is small, and so cos $\theta_e \approx 1$. When the loop is unlocked, the outputs from both phase detectors are beat-notes at the difference frequency, and the d-c output is almost zero.

Thus the filtered output of the quadrature detector provides a useful indication of lock. The magnitude of the output voltage, relative to that obtained from a noise-free stable input, provides a measure of the quality of lock. (If θ_e jitters, the average of cos θ_e is less than unity.) When used in this manner, the smoothed voltage is sometimes known as the "correlation" output. It is also possible to use the same voltage as a source of AGC control voltage. This topic has been analyzed by Victor and Brockman [Vic-2] and is covered further in Chapter 7 of this book.

Wide Bandwidth Methods

Rapid acquisition is possible by means other than sweeping; one method often used employs two different bandwidths. For acquisition the loop would have a wide bandwidth, whereas for tracking the loop would be considerably narrowed. From the formulas presented earlier (4-29, 4-30, 4-31) it may be seen that the pull-in range would be increased modestly, but the pull-in time would be dramatically reduced (inversely proportional to $\omega_n{}^3$). It should be apparent that increase of bandwidth can be successful only if signal-to-noise ratio is sufficiently large. If the bandwidth change brings the loop close to threshold, acquisition is not likely.

Bandwidth may be changed by any of several methods. A straightforward approach is to switch loop filter components. (It is usually advisable to switch the resistors only; if a new capacitor were switched in, the integrator charge would be disturbed, and the switching process might cause loss of lock.)

It is also feasible to switch the gain of the loop and change bandwidth. Richman [Ric-3] has examined both filter switching and gain switching and has devised some useful ways to approach the problem. The interested reader is referred to his article.

The switching command signal can be the lock indication voltage from the quadrature phase detector. When the loop is out of lock, the absence of indication voltage will permit the switches to be in their wideband position. When the loop locks, the indication voltage will appear and force the switches into their narrow-band position.

If coherent AGC is employed, the same effect can be obtained without switches. In the unlocked condition there is no AGC voltage and the signal level at the phase detector is large. When the loop locks, AGC voltage appears and reduces the applied signal voltage. Since phase detector gain—and therefore, loop gain—is proportional to signal level, the loop bandwidth and damping will both decrease automatically when the loop locks; no switches are needed.

One other method, sometimes used, employs a frequency discriminator in a conventional AFC arrangement, as in Figure 4-13. If the initial frequency difference is large, the discriminator pulls the VCO toward the

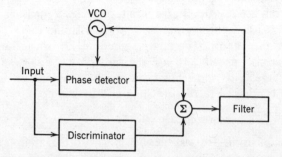

Figure 4-13   Discriminator-aided acquisition.

direction of lock. When the difference frequency comes within the grasp of the phase lock loop, the phase detector takes over and locks the loop. A conventional discriminator may be used when the locking frequency is fixed (as in a superheterodyne receiver). Otherwise, a device known as a quadricorrelator [Ric-2] can be used as a frequency-difference detector. Signal-to-noise ratio in the discriminator bandwidth (which is at least as wide as the desired acquisition bandwidth and is ordinarily many times greater than the phaselock-loop bandwidth) must be fairly high—+10 db or so. This is a severe restriction and renders the method useless for acquiring signals buried in the noise.

Chapter Five

Operation of loop components

In this chapter we discuss the operation and analysis of limiters, phase detectors, and VCO's. Other components are considered elsewhere.

5-1 Limiters

It is common practice in present-day phaselock-receiver design to place a bandpass limiter in front of the phase detector. The intent of the practice is not simply to limit the power delivered to the phase detector (although obviously this function is served) but to cause the receiver to adapt itself to varying signal-to-noise input conditions. This section describes the properties of a bandpass limiter and shows how these properties lead to useful adaptive behavior.

Davenport [Dav-1] performed the classic analysis of limiters, in which he found that a bandpass limiter degrades signal-to-noise ratio only slightly (1.06 db) for signals deeply embedded in the noise. This is extremely important, for if limiters were to cause significant degradation of SNR (as envelope detectors do below their threshold) they could not be used.

Davenport obtains exact expressions for output signal and noise as a function of input signal-to-noise ratio. These expressions contain infinite sums of confluent hypergeometric functions and are not much help to the practicing engineer. However, the relations are reasonably well approximated by

$$P_s \approx \frac{2L^2}{\pi}\left[\frac{4(\mathrm{SNR})_i/\pi}{4/\pi + (\mathrm{SNR})_i}\right] \tag{5-1}$$

and

$$P_n \approx \frac{2L^2}{\pi}\left[\frac{4/\pi}{1 + 2(\mathrm{SNR})_i}\right] \tag{5-2}$$

55

where P_s is the limiter output signal power, P_n is the output noise, $(SNR)_i$ is the signal-to-noise ratio at the input to the limiter, and L is the peak limiter output voltage before filtering.* According to these expressions, the total bandpass limiter output power, $P_s + P_n$, remains constant, within $\pm\frac{1}{2}$ db, over the full range of $(SNR)_i$.

Output signal-to-noise ratio is easily determined to be (approximately)

$$\frac{P_s}{P_n} = (SNR)_o \approx (SNR)_i \frac{1 + 2(SNR)_i}{4/\pi + (SNR)_i} \tag{5-3}$$

Figure 5-1 is a plot of SNR performance. At low $(SNR)_i$ the signal is degraded only by a factor of $\pi/4$, and at high $(SNR)_i$ it is actually enhanced by 3 db.

If the input is noise-free, the limiter delivers a signal power proportional to $8L^2/\pi^2$ to the phase detector. For this case the peak sinusoidal signal delivered to the phase detector is $4L/\pi$ volts (i.e., the peak of the fundamental component of a square wave of amplitude L.) This voltage is taken into account in the computation of detector gain factor, K_d [see (3-2), (3-3)].

Signal voltage delivered to the phase detector will be reduced as noise increases. This reduction of signal voltage reduces phase detector gain and therefore loop gain; in turn, loop bandwidth and damping are affected. The signal voltage will vary according to the "limiter signal suppression factor"

$$\alpha = \left(\frac{(SNR)_i}{4/\pi + (SNR)_i}\right)^{\frac{1}{2}} \tag{5-4}$$

It may be seen that $\alpha \leq 1$.

In all of the foregoing material, wherever loop gain $(K_o K_d)$ appears it must be multiplied by α if a limiter is used. For example, the d-c loop gain (see Chapter 2) is $K_v = \alpha K_o K_d F(0)$. Most of the other quantities derived in earlier chapters also have a simple dependence on α. In particular, ω_n and ζ are both proportional to $\sqrt{\alpha}$ so that bandwidth widens out and damping increases as input signal-to-noise ratio improves.

Noise bandwidth (3-12) is a function of ω_n and ζ; it also increases as $(SNR)_i$ increases. Minimum noise bandwidth will occur at minimum

---

* An ideal "snap-action" limiter is assumed. If input voltage is positive, the output voltage is $+L$; if instantaneous input voltage is negative, the output voltage is $-L$. Thus the output of the limiter itself is a square wave and this output is then filtered in a bandpass filter centered at the input frequency. The expressions for P_s and P_n are for the signal and noise at the output of the filter.

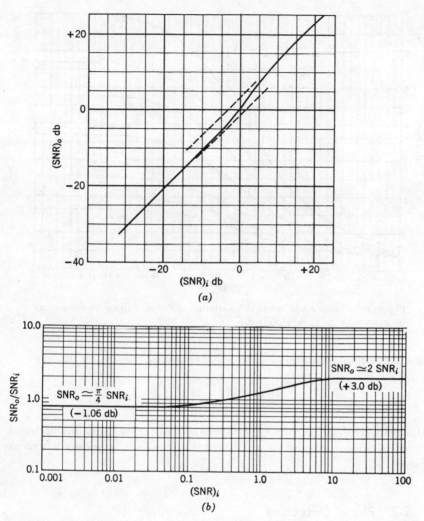

Figure 5-1 SNR performance of an ideal bandpass limiter. (*a*) Output versus input (*b*) Noise degradation.

signal level in any particular loop. This minimum signal is usually specified as the threshold and is designated here with the subscript T. Noise bandwidth may therefore be written as

$$B_L = B_{LT} \frac{[\alpha/\alpha_T + (4\zeta_T{}^2)^{-1}]}{[1 + (4\zeta_T{}^2)^{-1}]} \tag{5-5}$$

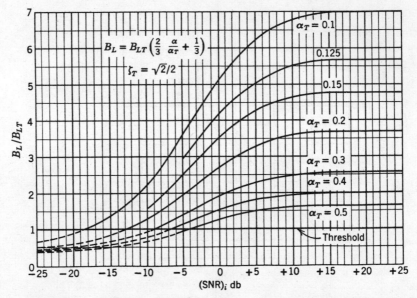

Figure 5-2   Loop noise bandwidth variation with input signal-to-noise ratio.
By permission of L. A. Hoffman.

In the common situation of $\zeta_T = 0.707$ the noise bandwidth becomes

$$B_L = \frac{B_{LT}}{3}\left(2\frac{\alpha}{\alpha_T} + 1\right) \qquad (5\text{-}5a)$$

Hoffman [Hof-1] has plotted noise bandwidth as a function of input signal-to-noise ratio for $\zeta_T = 0.707$; his curves are reproduced here as Figure 5-2.

5-2   Phase Detectors

Chapter 3 has shown that an ideal analog multiplier behaves as a phase detector and has a sinusoidal output characteristic. Any book on analog computers will provide analyses and circuits of multipliers. There has been some small use made of these devices, particularly at low frequencies. However, the typical multiplier is useful only at low frequencies and most phaselock work is done at higher frequencies. As a result, although a multiplier is a convenient mathematical model of a phase detector, the actual hardware used is more likely to have a different underlying mechanism.

(In very recent years field-effect transistors have been used as simple
effective multipliers [Hig-1, Mar-6]. There has been no report of their
application as phase detectors, but it is reasonable to expect good performance at higher frequencies than obtained hitherto.)

One of the more popular phase-detector circuits for receivers uses

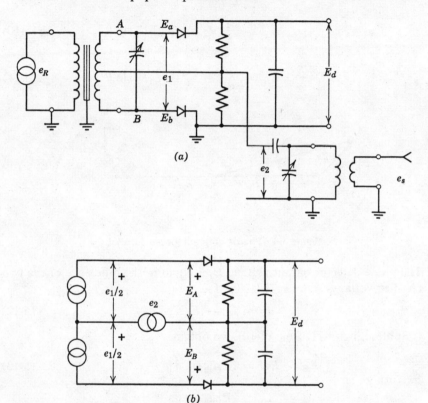

(a)

(b)

Figure 5-3   Diode phase detector. (a) Actual circuit (b) Simplified equivalent circuit.

balanced diode peak detectors, as shown in Figure 5-3. The two voltages
being compared may be represented as

$$e_1 = E_1 \sin \omega t \qquad (5\text{-}6)$$

$$e_2 = E_2 \cos (\omega t + \theta) \qquad (5\text{-}7)$$

The voltages actually applied to the two peak rectifiers are the sums

$$e_A = e_2 + \frac{e_1}{2} \qquad (5\text{-}8)$$

$$e_B = e_2 - \frac{e_1}{2} \qquad (5\text{-}9)$$

Rectified output voltages are equal to the amplitudes of each of the sums E_A and E_B. Their phasor diagram [Gru-1] is shown in Figure 5-4. The two circles of radius $r = E_2$ describe the path of voltages E_A and E_B, as the phase difference between e_1 and e_2 varies from 0 to 360 degrees.

According to the law of cosines and Figure 5-4,

$$E_A{}^2 = \frac{E_1{}^2}{4} + E_2{}^2 + E_1 E_2 \sin \theta \tag{5-10}$$

$$E_B{}^2 = \frac{E_1{}^2}{4} + E_2{}^2 - E_1 E_2 \sin \theta \tag{5-11}$$

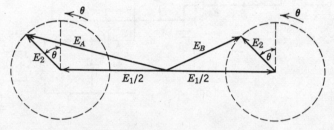

Figure 5-4   Phasor diagram, phase detector.

The phase detector output voltage E_d is equal to the difference of the two rectified voltages so that

$$E_d = E_A - E_B \tag{5-12}$$

Subtracting (5-11) from (5-10), we obtain

$$E_A{}^2 - E_B{}^2 = 2E_1 E_2 \sin \theta \tag{5-13}$$

Factoring

$$E_A - E_B = \frac{2E_1 E_2 \sin \theta}{E_A + E_B} \tag{5-14}$$

or

$$E_d = \frac{2E_1 E_2 \sin \theta}{E_A + E_B} \tag{5-15}$$

Now, if $E_1/2 \gg E_2$, then

$$E_A + E_B \approx E_1 \tag{5-16}$$

and

$$E_d \approx \frac{2E_1 E_2 \sin \theta}{E_1} \tag{5-17}$$

The detector output voltage then becomes

$$\boxed{E_d \approx 2E_2 \sin \theta} \tag{5-18}$$

Equation 5-18 shows that E_d is directly proportional to E_2 but is independent of E_1 when $E_1/2 \gg E_2$.* Also, it can be seen from (5-18) that $E_d = 0$ when $\theta = 0°$ and $E_d = 2E_2$ when $\theta = \pm 90°$.

Several important conclusions can be drawn from the preceding derivation of (5-18):

1. If $E_1/2 \gg E_2$, then detector operation becomes independent of E_1. The larger E_1 becomes (without causing diode breakdown), the more accurate (5-18) becomes.

2. If E_d is to be independent of signal amplitude variation, E_2 must be held constant.

3. The phase detector can be used as an amplitude-sensitive device (or AGC detector) by maintaining $\theta = 90°$ and allowing E_2 to vary as a function of input signal level.

4. For E_d to have zero output with no signal input the phase detector must be carefully balanced with respect to the reference input.

Ideally, the phase detector is perfectly balanced and even in the presence of a noisy signal has a d-c output proportional to the signal phase only. In practice, of course, this is not the case. Balance can never be perfect and some offset in the PD output is inevitable. A fixed offset comes from unbalance with respect to the reference source E_1, whereas an offset dependent on SNR arises from unbalances of rectified noise.

If total offset exceeds the maximum value of E_d generated by the signal, the loop cannot lock; the signal-to-noise ratio at which offset becomes excessive is the threshold of the phase detector. This PD threshold must be distinguished from the loop threshold discussed in Chapter 3. A PD threshold develops because of imperfections of real world phase detectors, whereas the loop threshold is inherent in the phaselock process. Needless to say, a proper design should guarantee that the PD threshold is well below the loop threshold. For typical diode circuits of the type shown in Figure 5-3 the PD threshold can be expected to be near an input SNR of -30 db.

An upper frequency limit on this type of phase detector is set by the reverse recovery time of the diodes. At sufficiently high frequencies the reverse recovery is a significant portion of a cycle period and rectifier performance deteriorates. For fast computer diodes of the 1N914 class

---

* An analysis that does not make this approximation and takes nonideal diode characteristics into account has been performed by Dishington [Dis-1].

precision phase detectors (those used in narrow-band loops with high noise levels) have been built at frequencies as high as 10 mc. The same quality of diodes can be used in circuits up to 30 mc, provided very narrow bandwidths and high noise levels are not encountered.

A few diode types have appreciably faster response than the 1N914; presumably, they could be used in higher-frequency phase detectors. Precision circuits capable of operating at 90 to 100 mc would be very convenient.

Phase detectors can be constructed for use at VHF and microwave frequencies. Instead of a balanced transformer, as in Figure 5-3, a four-port hybrid, either transmission line or waveguide, is used. The two inputs are connected to opposite ports, and a pair of diode detectors is connected to the other two ports. Error voltage is the difference between the d-c outputs of the two detectors. (A balanced mixer with signal frequency equal to LO frequency could be a phase detector.)

At such high frequencies the diodes act as nonlinear resistors (approximately square law) rather than rectifiers. Efficiency is not high and, since microwave diode breakdown voltage is usually low, maximum available output voltage (and phase-detector gain) tend to be low. These phase detectors have been used in wideband applications in which noise is not a problem. The analysis of their operation is similar to that presented for the peak rectifier type of detector.

Another common type of phase detector consists of almost nothing but a switch. The device that functions as the switch may be a transistor, a diode quad, or even a mechanical switch or chopper. The switch is driven synchronously with the input signal; on alternate half-cycles it allows the input either to pass or not to pass.

Figure 5-5 illustrates the nomenclature and typical waveforms. If the input is $E_s \cos(\omega t + \theta)$ and the switch changes state at the zero crossings of $\sin \omega t$, the output is $E_s \cos(\omega t + \theta)$ for $0 < \omega t < \pi$ and zero for $\pi < \omega t < 2\pi$. The d-c output of the detector is

$$E_d = \frac{E_s}{2\pi} \int_0^\pi \cos(\omega t + \theta) \, d\omega t$$

$$= -\frac{E_s}{\pi} \sin \theta \tag{5-19}$$

Figure 5-5 illustrates a half-wave detector; if a full-wave detector were used instead, the d-c output would be doubled (which is of no great consequence), and the ripple frequency would also be doubled. In extreme wideband loops there will often be problems of phase-detector ripple getting to the VCO and causing phase jitter. In such cases additional filtering cannot be used without narrowing (and possibly unstabilizing)

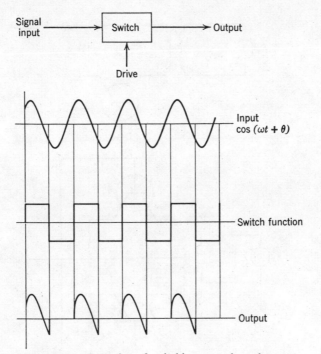

Figure 5-5   Operation of switching-type phase-detector.

the loop. Only ingenious design of the phase detector can relieve the problem, and full-wave operation is a first step in the proper direction.

Several commonly used switching-type phase-detector circuits are shown in Figure 5-6.

We have analyzed three different types of phase detector and in each case have found a sinusoidal characteristic. It can readily be shown that the form of the characteristic is due to the sine wave input and not to the circuit itself. For example, if square wave inputs* were to be applied to any of the three types of circuit, the output characteristic would be triangular rather than sinusoidal (see Figure 5-7b). Square waves may be obtained by passing both inputs to a phase detector through wideband limiters.

Linearity in the triangular case is near-perfect for phase angles as large as 90 degrees—a significant improvement over the sinusoidal. When a loop is intended as an FM discriminator, linearity is an important feature, and the triangular characteristic is widely used.

---

* Digital operation is approached when both inputs are square. A phase detector degenerates to an Exclusive-OR gate whose error output is the time average of its two logic states.

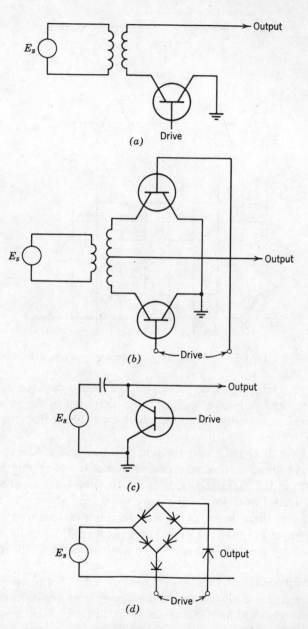

Figure 5-6 Phase detector circuits. (*a*) Half-wave series transistor (*b*) Full-wave transistor (*c*) Shunt transistor (*d*) Diode quad.

It would be desirable to extend the linear range even beyond 90 degrees if possible. A phase-detection scheme known as "Tanlock" [Bal-1, Rob-2] provides a measure of improvement. In this method the control voltage has the form

$$E_d = \frac{(1 + x) \sin \theta_e}{1 + x \cos \theta_e}$$

which can be shown to have a greater linear range than $\sin \theta_e$ for proper choice of x. The functions $\sin \theta_e$ and $\cos \theta_e$ are obtained from conventional

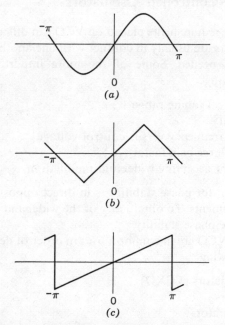

Figure 5-7 Phase-detector characteristics. (a) Sinusoidal (b) Triangular (c) Sawtooth.

phase detectors driven in quadrature, and the quotient is obtained from an analog divider (a multiplier in a feedback loop). The greater linear range not only reduces distortion of the recovered modulation, but from experimental results has shown improvements in noise threshold, hold-in range, and pull-out frequency.

There are special conditions for which a sawtooth characteristic (Figure 5-7c) is possible. A phase detector that provides this characteristic can be nothing more complicated than a flip-flop [Byr-1, Gol-2]. For such a detector the signal input sets the FF once in each cycle, and the VCO toggles (changes the state of) the FF once in each cycle. Output error voltage is the average of the output of the FF. Analysis (or reference to Byrne) will show that a sawtooth characteristic is obtained.

Besides the obvious advantage of linearity, this type of phase detector will also have improved tracking, hold-in, and pull-in characteristics [Bar-1, Gol-3]. Unfortunately, the two signals must be of a quality that will trigger a flip-flop reliably. Input signal-to-noise ratio must be high, and therefore threshold will be high. Such a phase detector is of no value if signal must be recovered from a larger noise.

5-3　Voltage-Controlled Oscillators

There are many requirements placed on VCO's in different applications. These requirements are usually in conflict with one another, and therefore a compromise is needed. Some of the more important requirements include the following:

1. Large electrical tuning range
2. Phase stability
3. Linearity of frequency versus control voltage
4. Reasonably large gain factor (K_o)
5. Capability for accepting wideband modulation.

The requirement for phase stability is in direct opposition to all of the other four requirements. To obtain any of the wideband features we must inevitably sacrifice phase stability.

Three types of VCO are in common use; in order of decreasing stability they are the following:

1. Crystal oscillators (VCXO)
2. LC oscillators
3. RC multivibrators

In today's technology the stablest crystal oscillators are those using high-Q, vacuum mounted, 2.5- or 5.0-mc, fifth-overtone, AT-cut crystals [War-1, Syk-1, And-1, Jpl-6, Jpl-7].

A circuit commonly used (Figure 5-8a) is a variation on the familiar Pierce crystal oscillator [Fel-1, Jpl-7, Smi-1]. The crystal is operated in its series mode, and capacitors C_1 and C_2 adjust the amount of feedback. A varactor diode provides a small variation of C_2 and results in a pulling of the oscillation frequency.

The tuning range of this circuit is very small when high-Q crystals are used. To obtain a greater range it is common practice to use ordinary AT-cut crystals in their fundamental mode* in the circuit of Figure 5-8b. The crystal here is also operated in its series mode. The varactor is in

---

* Overtone crystals have a narrower pulling range than fundamental crystals.

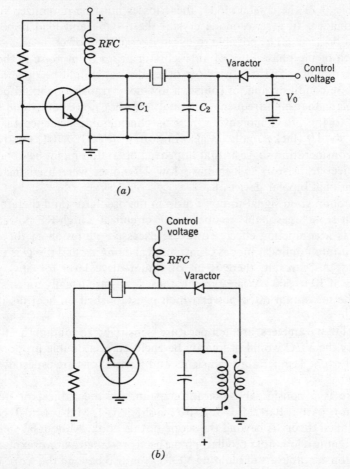

(a)

(b)

Figure 5-8   VXCO circuits. (a) Modified Pierce oscillator (b) Grounded-base oscillator.

series with the crystal and effectively varies the resonant frequency over some range greater than the first circuit.

Phase-stability is enhanced by a number of factors:

1. High-Q in the crystal and circuit
2. Low noise in the amplifier portion
3. Temperature stability
4. Mechanical stability

The precision 5-mc crystals mentioned have an unloaded Q of approximately 2×10^6. Other crystals can be expected to have unloaded Q's in the range of 10,000 to 200,000. Circuit losses will inevitably degrade the intrinsic Q of the crystal alone; these losses must be minimized for best performance. In a series-mode crystal the driving and load impedances should be as small as possible to avoid degradation of Q.

Much of the phase jitter of an oscillator arises from noise in the associated amplifier. The transistor (or other device) should be operated in a low-noise condition and, of course, a low-noise transistor should be used. It is plain that high-frequency thermal and shot noise contribute significantly to the jitter; moreover, there is considerable evidence that low-frequency, $1/f$ (flicker) noise is also important [Fey-1, Att-1, Gri-1]. (The latter consideration suggests that improved operation might be obtained if field-effect transistors, which have low $1/f$ noise, were used instead of conventional bipolar devices.)

To obtain good signal-to-noise ratio in the oscillator (and therefore low jitter) it seems reasonable to operate the circuit at a high RF power level. There is a competing effect, however; excessive vibration of the crystal drives it into nonlinear modes of mechanical damping and the Q is thereby reduced. As a result, there is an optimum drive level for any crystal. Powers of 10 to 500 μW are typical; these levels are usually much smaller than the maximum rated power which is established on heat dissipation limitations.

Crystal parameters are temperature sensitive; to obtain best phase stability the VCO would ordinarily be enclosed in a double proportional-control oven. Temperature transients and fluctuations are especially to be avoided.

There is a considerable literature extant on the subject of noise in oscillators [Att-1, Bar-2, Eds-1, Esp-1, Gol-5, Gri-1, Mal-1, Mul-1, San-2]; the detailed theory is beyond the scope of this book. Although some rules for designing a low-jitter oscillator have been presented here, an explanation of the considerable art of building VCXO's is also beyond the scope of this book. (Furthermore, it tends to be in the nature of trade secrets.)

We are concerned with the behavior of a VCO in a phaselocked loop. Suppose a loop is receiving a perfectly stable, noise-free signal but that the VCO has some inherent jitter ϕ_o. The feedback action of the loop causes the VCO to track the input and thus the actual phase error between input and VCO will be less than ϕ_o. (Full phase jitter ϕ_o will appear only when the loop is open.)

It may be shown readily that the actual loop jitter θ_p is given by

$$\frac{\theta_p}{\phi_o}(s) = -[1 - H(s)] \tag{5-20}$$

which is, in essence, the same as the loop-error response (eq. 2-7 and

Figure 2-4). Loop-phase fluctuation is

$$\overline{\theta_p^2} = \frac{1}{2\pi} \int_0^\infty \Phi_o(\omega) |1 - H(\omega)|^2 \, d\omega \qquad (5\text{-}21)$$

where $\Phi_o(\omega)$ is the spectral density of the oscillator phase jitter in (radians)^2 per Hertz.

It is evident that loop jitter will be zero if $H(\omega) = 1$; that is, if the loop tracks the input perfectly, there is no error. This condition requires that loop bandwidth be infinite. For the practical finite-bandwidth loop, the error will not be zero; there will be an inverse relationship between bandwidth and loop jitter Fragmentary empirical evidence [Jpl-6] suggests the form

$$\overline{\theta_p^2} = \frac{J}{(B_L)^\gamma} \qquad (5\text{-}22)$$

where J is a measure of the noisiness of the particular oscillator and γ is a constant depending on the noise spectrum of the oscillator jitter. A value of $\gamma = 2.4$ for bandwidths in the range of $\frac{1}{3}$ to 50 Hz for the types of crystal and circuit mentioned has been measured. The same reference reports that rms phase jitter as low as 0.005 degree in a bandwidth of $B_L = 1.5$ Hz has been achieved with a precision 5-mc crystal.

As loop bandwidth is reduced further and further, the loop phase jitter continually increases. If bandwidth is made too narrow, the jitter becomes excessive (tracking is too sluggish) and the loop will not be able to maintain lock. A measure of the quality of an oscillator is the minimum bandwidth for which it still remains locked.

When wide tuning range becomes more important than stability, other oscillator types must be used. We have heard that X-cut crystals in parallel-mode circuits have been employed in very wide range VCXO's, but as far as is known extreme tuning limits of 0.25 to 0.5 per cent of oscillator frequency are all that has been achieved.

If a wider range is needed, an LC oscillator must be used. In this application, the standard Hartley, Colpitts, and Clapp circuits make their appearance. Tuning may be accomplished by means of a varactor, although saturable inductors have also been used. Some early loops made use of "reactance tubes," but this method became obsolete with the disappearance of tubes from low-power circuits. (With the recent advent of the field-effect transistor, the reactance modulator might conceivably make a limited comeback. However, the convenience of varactors would make this event unlikely.)

Finally, when stability is of little importance, large tuning range is needed, and low cost is a factor, relaxation oscillators such as multi-vibrators and blocking oscillators are used. The operating frequency of practical relaxation oscillators has been limited to a few megacycles. Linearity of frequency versus control voltage (or current) is generally excellent.

To measure phase jitter it is necessary to compare two oscillators. Because both will have jitter, it is impossible to determine which of the two is responsible. If the oscillators are identical, half the mean-square jitter can be assigned to each.

To avoid problems with frequency differences one oscillator must be locked to the other by means of a narrow-band, phaselock loop. Phase jitter is then measured at the output of the loop phase detector.

Good quality oscillators will exhibit little jitter at their fundamental frequencies in loops of reasonable bandwidth. To magnify the oscillator jitter their frequencies can be multiplied many times and the comparison is then made in the microwave region [Vic-1].

Chapter Six

Optimization of loop performance

Two general principles may be abstracted from the preceding chapters:

1. To minimize output phase jitter due to external noise the loop bandwidth should be made as narrow as possible.

2. To minimize transient error due to signal modulation, to minimize output jitter due to internal oscillator noise, or to obtain best tracking and acquisition properties the loop bandwidth should be made as wide as possible.

These principles are directly opposed to one another; improvement in one type of performance can come only at the expense of degrading the other, and therefore some compromise between the two is always necessary. Almost always there is a compromise that is "best" in some sense; this compromise is called "optimum."

It must be recognized that there is no unique optimum result that applies under all conditions. On the contrary, there are many possible results, depending on the criteria of performance, the nature of the input signal, and any restrictions placed on loop configuration.

The best-known optimization is that derived by Jaffe and Rechtin [Jaf-1] following the Wiener method.* Their criterion of loop performance is the mean-square loop error

$$\sum^2 = \overline{\theta_{no}^2} + \lambda^2 E_T^2 \tag{6-1}$$

where $\overline{\theta_{no}^2}$ is the phase jitter due to noise (3-13), and E_T^2 is a measure of the total transient error:

$$E_T^2 = \int_0^\infty \theta_e^2(t)\, dt \tag{6-2}$$

---

* Details of the Wiener method are far beyond the scope of this book. For an extensive exposition of the subject, see Y. W. Lee, *Statistical Theory of Communication*, Wiley, New York, 1960, Chapters 14 through 17. A more directly applicable explanation may be found in Rechtin's notes [Rec-1].

where $\theta_e(t)$ is the instantaneous phase error in the loop due to transients. The quantity λ is a Lagrangian multiplier which establishes the relative proportions of noise and transient error that are to be permitted. [Notice that λ^2 has dimensions of $(\text{time})^{-1}$—that is, frequency.]

In the Wiener optimization method the known quantities are the spectra of the signal and noise, whereas the criterion of performance is the mean-square error $\sum^2$. The result of the method is a description of an "optimum" filter whose output provides a minimum mean-square error.

Jaffe and Rechtin have assumed white noise and three different types of modulation at the input; phase step, frequency step, and frequency ramp. For each condition they arrive at an optimum loop transfer function $H(s)$ and the corresponding transfer function for the loop filter $F(s)$. Results are summarized in Table 6-1.

Table 6-1   Wiener—Optimized Loops

Input	Optimum $H(s)$	$F(s)$	Optimum Bandwidth
Phase Step $\theta_i(t) = \Delta\theta$	$\dfrac{\omega_1}{s + \omega_1}$	$\dfrac{\omega_1}{K_oK_d}$	$\omega_1 = \Delta\theta\lambda\left(\dfrac{2P_s}{W_o}\right)^{1/2}$
Frequency step $\theta_i(t) = \Delta\omega t$	$\dfrac{\omega_n^2 + \sqrt{2}\omega_n s}{\omega_n^2 + \sqrt{2}\,\omega_n s + s^2}$	$\dfrac{\omega_n^2 + \sqrt{2}\omega_n s}{K_oK_d s}$	$\omega_n^2 = \Delta\omega\lambda\left(\dfrac{2P_s}{W_o}\right)^{1/2}$
Frequency ramp $\theta_i(t) = \dfrac{\Delta\dot{\omega}t^2}{2}$	$\dfrac{\omega_3^3 + 2\omega_3^2 s + 2\omega_3 s^2}{\omega_3^3 + 2\omega_3^2 s + 2\omega_3 s^2 + s^3}$	$\dfrac{\omega_3^3 + 2\omega_3^2 s + 2\omega_3 s^2}{K_oK_d s^2}$	$\omega_3^3 = \Delta\dot{\omega}\lambda\left(\dfrac{2P_s}{W_o}\right)^{1/2}$

P_s = input signal power
W_o = input noise spectral density (one-sided)

For the three different types of input the optimum filter types are first-, second-, and third-order loops, respectively; the Wiener method specifies optimum filter shape as well as bandwidth. In the optimum second-order loop (of greatest interest because of its widespread usage) damping factor is $\zeta = 0.707$. The optimum third-order loop has complex zeros which are not usually convenient to mechanize.

It will be noted that optimum bandwidth is a function of the input signal-to-noise ratio. To minimize the total error the loop should be capable of measuring SNR and readjusting its bandwidth for optimum performance. To perform this optimum adaptation exactly would be a complex and difficult task; as far as is known, there has never been a serious attempt at perfect adaptation.

One reason for the lack of effort is that Jaffe and Rechtin discovered that near-optimum adaptation may be achieved by very simple means: namely, use of a bandpass limiter before the phase detector. In Chapter 5, we found that the presence of a limiter causes loop bandwidth and damping to vary as a function of input SNR. This variation is not optimum (damping should remain constant, and the variation of ω_n should have a different form), but it is sufficiently close to optimum to be useful. Limiters are widely used in sensitive phaselock receivers.*

It is of interest to observe that the definition of $E_T{}^2$ given here is such that steady-state error must be zero. If this were not true, $E_T{}^2$ would be infinite. If some other definition of transient error were to be used (e.g., peak error), it is probable that different optimum results would be obtained.

The Wiener analysis is strictly applicable only to linear systems; to apply it to the phaselock loop requires that the linear approximation be made. Furthermore, Jaffe and Rechtin's exact results are applicable only if noise is white (see [Nis-1] for an approach to correlated noise input), when the input is one of the three specific types listed here, and when the error criterion is that given in (6-1) (see [Gol-4] as an example of different input and different error criterion); all of this is to say that we have so far shown only *an* optimum (or rather three optimum loops) and not *the* optimum loop, even in the restricted category of Wiener filters.

In practice, when narrow bandwidth is needed, a second-order loop is the type most commonly used. A first-order loop necessitates a major sacrifice of hold-in range and has poor phase-slope properties, whereas a third-order loop is more complicated and harder to analyze and can become unstable if not treated properly. (However, both first- and third-order loops have their uses in which they will substantially outperform the second-order loop.) For the remainder of this chapter we restrict ourselves to the second-order loop and give examples of the different optimizations that are possible.

Suppose that the natural frequency is determined by some well-defined dynamic feature of the input signal. For example, a satellite will exhibit a very definite rate of change of Doppler frequency; if a limit is placed on the permissible acceleration error, ω_n is immediately fixed. Given this value of ω_n, what value of damping factor results in the least phase jitter

---

* It should be possible to obtain similar performance from wideband (noncoherent) AGC, for the same phenomenon of signal suppression occurs. There is a 1-db advantage in wideband AGC in favor of low SNR because the limiter causes 1-db SNR degradation and the AGC does not. Coherent AGC on the other hand, maintains signal level constant at the phase detector and therefore has no adaptive bandwidth properties. There are situations in which coherent AGC and limiting are used simultaneously [Bro-1]. In that case the limiter provides bandwidth adaptation. The purpose of the AGC might be to prevent limiting at places in the receiver other than the limiter, to standardize signal level in order to recover and measure amplitude modulation, to measure signal level, or to adjust gain of auxiliary channels (e.g., antenna angle-tracking loops).

due to noise? The answer, referring to Figure 3-1, is obviously $\zeta = 0.5$, for this is the value that minimizes noise bandwidth.

For another possibility, suppose that noise bandwidth is fixed by, let us say, restrictions on the maximum allowable phase noise jitter. What value of damping will permit the largest frequency step $\Delta\omega$ without the loop's being pulled out of lock, even temporarily? In (3-12) the noise bandwidth was found to be

$$B_L = \frac{\omega_n}{2}\left(\zeta + \frac{1}{4\zeta}\right)$$

and (4-2) approximates pull-out frequency as

$$\Delta\omega_{\mathrm{PO}} = 1.8\omega_n(\zeta + 1)$$

Elimination of ω_n between these equations yields

$$\Delta\omega_{\mathrm{PO}} = \frac{3.6B_L(\zeta + 1)}{\zeta + 1/4\zeta} \tag{6-3}$$

By differentiating $\Delta\omega_{\mathrm{PO}}$ with respect to ζ, setting the derivative equal to zero, and solving we obtain $\zeta = 0.81$ as the damping that maximizes pull-out frequency. This maximum value is $\Delta\omega_{\mathrm{PO}} \approx 5.82B_L$ rad/sec. Pull-out frequency is $5.79B_L$ at $\zeta = 0.707$, $5.40B_L$ at $\zeta = 0.5$, and $5.76B_L$ at $\zeta = 1.0$, so that it is hardly worthwhile to bother to optimize pull-out as such.

This finding tends to illustrate a common property of optima; the performance criterion quantity tends to change very slowly near the optimum, so that there is no need to adjust the loop to attain exactly the best performance. The extremum will usually be quite broad.

Hoffman [Hof-1] has derived another optimization that appears to have greater value than the preceding. A phaselock receiver is often required to track an accelerating transmitter (either true acceleration of a missile or apparent acceleration of a satellite) with a second-order loop. What acceleration error*—and, therefore, what loop bandwidth—should be used to achieve "optimum" performance?

First it is necessary to arrive at a criterion of performance. Rechtin's criterion cannot be applied because the nonzero, steady-state acceleration error would lead to an infinite integrated-square transient error. Hoffman used noise threshold as his criterion. His definition of threshold is an empirical relation taken from Martin [Mar-3] which states that at threshold

$$\theta_a + \sigma\theta_{no} = \frac{\pi}{2} \tag{6-4}$$

---

* If acceleration error is a serious problem, consideration should be given to a third-order loop to reduce the steady-state error to zero.

where θ_a is the acceleration error (4-7a), θ_{no} is the rms noise jitter in the loop (3-13), and σ is a confidence factor that takes account of the fact that peak noise considerably exceeds the rms value. Equation 6-4 states that threshold error is exceeded if the sum of the individual errors exceeds 90 degrees.

The quantity to be optimized is the input signal power P_s. From the discussion of behavior of θ_{no} in Chapter 3 and (3-15), an expression of

$$\overline{\theta_{no}^2} = \frac{\xi^2}{(\text{SNR})_L} \tag{6-5}$$

may be deduced. [For $(\text{SNR})_L > 10$, $\xi^2 = \frac{1}{2}$; for $(\text{SNR})_L = 1$, $\xi^2 \approx 1$. The factor ξ is itself a function of $(\text{SNR})_L$, but we shall regard it as essentially constant.]

From (3-16), $(\text{SNR})_L = P_s/2B_L W_i$, where W_i is the input noise density. Equation 6-4 may now be written as

$$\theta_a + \sigma\xi\left(\frac{2B_L W_i}{P_s}\right)^{\frac{1}{2}} = \frac{\pi}{2} \tag{6-6}$$

Using (3-12) and (4-7a), we may eliminate B_L from (6-6), leaving

$$\theta_a + \sigma\xi\left[\frac{W_i}{P_s}\left(\zeta + \frac{1}{4\zeta}\right)\sqrt{\frac{\Delta\dot\omega}{\theta_a}}\right]^{\frac{1}{2}} = \frac{\pi}{2} \tag{6-7}$$

Solving for signal power required at threshold yields

$$P_s = \frac{\sigma^2\xi^2(\zeta + 1/4\zeta)(\Delta\dot\omega/\theta_a)^{\frac{1}{2}} W_i}{(\pi/2 - \theta_a)^2} \tag{6-8}$$

When P_s is minimized with respect to θ_a, the surprising result is that $\theta_a = \pi/10$ (i.e., 18 degrees), independent of σ, ξ, ζ, or W_i. This exact result depends on two approximations: using (6-4) as the definition of threshold and assuming that ξ is constant. An exact analysis, if one should ever be discovered, would probably yield a somewhat different result, but presumably not very different.

Calculation of the minimum P_s still requires that a confidence factor σ be specified and a suitable value for ξ deduced. The latter, which might require an iterative process, is complicated by the fact that the functional dependence of ξ on $(\text{SNR})_L$ is not known within limits closer than about ± 1 db. Also, refer to Chapter 3 for a discussion of fundamental difficulties in defining θ_{no}.

From (6-8) it may be seen that P_s can also be minimized with respect to damping factor; the optimum value is clearly $\zeta = 0.5$. Hoffman arbitrarily uses $\zeta = 0.707$ and thereby obtains a threshold power that is higher than optimum by 0.26 db.

Hoffman's approach suggests another possible optimization to be used when acceleration error in a second-order loop must be considered. Suppose that $(SNR)_L$ is reasonably large (>10) and let the criterion of performance be

$$\Sigma^2 = \theta_a^{\ 2} + \overline{\theta_{no}^{\ 2}} = \frac{(\Delta\dot\omega)^2}{\omega_n^{\ 4}} + \frac{B_L W_i}{P_s}$$

$$= \frac{(\Delta\dot\omega)^2(\zeta + 1/4\zeta)^4}{16B_L^{\ 4}} + \frac{B_L W_i}{P_s} \tag{6-9}$$

which is to be minimized with respect to B_L and ζ. It is immediately evident that the optimum damping is $\zeta = 0.5$ and that the usual differentiation will yield

$$B_L^{\ 5} = \frac{P_s(\Delta\dot\omega)^2}{4W_i} \tag{6-10}$$

for optimum loop-noise bandwidth.

We end the chapter with one more example that may be useful. Suppose the signal transmitter is essentially stationary with respect to the receiver so that dynamic phase errors may be neglected: a situation that could occur in tracking a synchronous satellite. Also, if a vehicle is on a ballistic trajectory, its apparent acceleration can be predicted with great accuracy. The VCO can be externally programmed to follow this prediction closely, and the loop is required only to track the error between predicted and actual trajectories.

The criterion of performance is taken as the total mean-square phase jitter in the loop, which, of course, is to be minimized. Jitter is composed of a part caused by external noise (3-13) and a part caused by inherent VCO jitter (5-22). The total mean-square jitter is

$$\Sigma^2 = \frac{W_i B_L}{P_s} + \frac{J}{(B_L)^\gamma} \tag{6-11}$$

from which the optimum bandwidth may be found to be

$$B_L^{\gamma+1} = \frac{\gamma J P_s}{W_i} \tag{6-12}$$

and the minimum mean-square error is

$$\Sigma^2 = (\gamma J)^{1/(\gamma+1)}\left(\frac{W_i}{P_s}\right)^{\gamma/(\gamma+1)}\left(1 + \frac{1}{\gamma}\right) \tag{6-13}$$

To summarize, consider the following points:

1. There is no uniquely optimum loop, nor is there a unique optimization procedure.

2. A criterion of performance must be defined. This criterion depends on the conditions of operation of the loop and the requirements placed on it. From the examples given here it may be seen that no general rule can be used in establishing the criterion.

3. Once an optimum is found, it is not usually necessary to adjust the loop parameters exactly to their optimum values. It is common for an extremum to be quite broad: in fact, to such an extent that moderate departure from optimum parameters has little adverse effect on loop performance.

Chapter Seven

Phaselock receivers

A simplified block diagram of a superheterodyne phaselocked receiver is shown in Figure 7-1. The incoming signal at frequency f_1 is mixed with a heterodyning local injection at frequency f_2 derived from a harmonic of the VCO at frequency f_2/N. Intermediate frequency is $f_3 = f_1 - f_2$ or $f_2 - f_1$, depending on whether low-side or high-side injection is used.

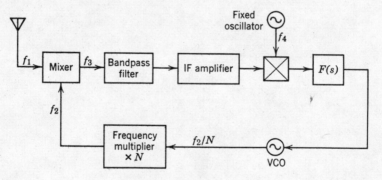

Figure 7-1　Phaselock receiver.

The IF amplifier may be entirely conventional, but its filtering and amplifying properties have been shown in separate boxes here. A fixed oscillator at frequency f_4 is compared against IF amplifier output in a phase detector; the loop is closed through the loop filter, VCO, frequency multiplier, and mixer. In the locked condition it is necessary that $f_3 = f_4$; the input frequency therefore is $f_1 = f_2 + f_4$ or $f_1 - f_4$ for low-side or high-side injection, respectively.

Presence of the new elements—particularly the frequency multiplier and IF filter—can have a substantial effect on the performance and analysis of the loop. In preceding chapters gain of the VCO (K_o rad/sec/ volt) has been considered a property of the VCO itself, not including any subsequent multiplications. When a multiplier is used, the deviation of the VCO is increased by the multiplying factor N before injection into the mixer. Effective VCO gain is therefore really NK_o. When a multiplier is used, K_o must be replaced by NK_o wherever it appears in any equation.

7-1   Effects of IF Amplifier

Inclusion of the IF filter can have much more far-reaching effects. We discuss phase-slope, noise, analysis of the filter, loop stability, and possibility of false locks.

Phase-Slope

A narrow-band IF filter necessarily has a steep phase-slope. If the frequency of the signal passing through the filter changes, the phase shift of the signal will also change. Such phase variations cause an error in the interpretation of any information being carried by signal phase; Doppler shift would be an example.

In the receiver shown in Figure 7-1 the intermediate frequency in the locked-loop condition is constrained to be exactly equal to the frequency of the fixed oscillator that feeds the phase detector. For this reason, although the IF filter may itself have a steep phase slope, the signal will suffer no phase change as its frequency changes.

In other mechanizations of phaselock receivers no fixed oscillator is used. Instead, a low harmonic of the VCO is injected into the phase detector, and the intermediate frequency is variable—although not nearly so much as the input frequency. Under these circumstances the signal will suffer some phase change; the tolerable amount of change must be taken into account in the receiver design.

Noise

The effect of the IF amplifier on noise is best treated by means of an example. Suppose a signal could arise anywhere within a 500-kc range and that the loop is designed for $B_L = 25$ Hz $(2B_L = 50$ Hz$)$. In a simple loop, not including an IF filter, the input bandwidth to the loop would have to be at least 500 kc merely to pass the input signal. Signal-to-noise ratio in the 500-kc bandwidth would be 40 db lower than SNR in the loop.

At nominal loop threshold of 0 db the input SNR would be -40 db. However, threshold of typical phase detectors is on the order of -30 db, and conservative design would have them operate at no worse than -20 db. With the wide input bandwidth, imperfections of the phase detector will limit obtainable performance, whereas a properly designed equipment should be limited by inherent properties of a loop.

The typical solution to this problem is to utilize an IF bandpass filter that is much narrower than the required full input bandwidth. If, for example, an IF passband of 2.5 kc were used, the SNR at the input to the phase detector would be only 17 db below loop SNR, and at nominal loop threshold the phase detector would be some 13 db above its threshold.

It should be evident that as soon as a reasonable margin against phase detector threshold has been obtained there is little to be gained by narrowing the IF bandwidth any further. Not only is a narrower filter more costly, but it can make the loop oscillate. The problem of loop stability is discussed in some detail in the following paragraphs.

IF Filter Analysis

It is first necessary to determine a method of bringing the IF bandpass filter into the loop analysis. To this end, consider the hypothetical test setup of Figure 7-2. We wish to determine the effect of the filter on the

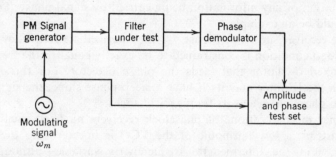

Figure 7-2   Measurement of modulation transfer function.

modulation of the test signal. Specifically, the amplitude and phase of the modulation output compared with the modulation input, as a function of modulation frequency, are desired. The result, which can be considered as a modulation transfer function denoted $F_m(s)$, is stated but not proved.   If (1) the filter has a narrow, symmetrical passband, (2) the signal generator is tuned to the center frequency of the filter, and (3) the modulation deviation is very small, the approximate modulation transfer function is obtained by translating the actual filter transfer function to zero frequency and discarding the response at negative frequencies. This translation is illustrated in Figure 7-3.

Now suppose the open-loop response of the loop of Figure 7-1 were to be measured (at least conceptually, if not in actual practice) by opening the loop somewhere in its low-frequency portion and applying a low-frequency sinusoidal test signal. Total open-loop response will consist of the product of the normal response of the loop $F(s)/s$ and the modulation transfer function of the IF filter, or $F_m(s) F(s)/s$.

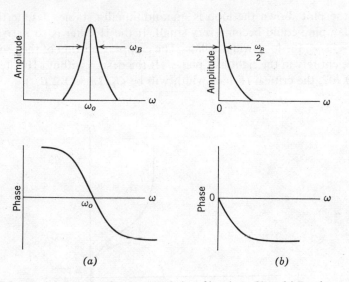

Figure 7-3   Modulation transfer characteristics of bandpass filter. (a) Bandpass transfer function (b) Equivalent modulation transfer function.

Stability

If the IF filter response (and therefore the modulation transfer function) are known analytically, the effect on loop response can be studied by means of a root-locus plot. Perhaps the most important filter from a practical viewpoint is a single-tuned circuit with 3-db bandwidth of ω_B radians per second. The equivalent modulation transfer function has a single pole at $s = -\omega_B/2$.

To provide a numerical example, suppose that $\omega_B/2 = 5/\tau_2$; where τ_2 in a second-order loop is defined in Chapter 3. (This is equivalent to $\omega_B/2\pi = 4.25B_L$ if the loop is designed for damping of 0.707.) Figure 7-4 is a root-locus plot of a second-order loop that includes such an IF filter.

The additional pole has split open the circle of the basic loop and pushed back the cut ends to be asymptotic to a vertical line at $-2/\tau_2$. In general, for any location of the extra pole at $-\omega_B/2$ the vertical line is at $\frac{1}{2}(\omega_B/2 - 1/\tau_2)$.

Obviously the IF filter has had a drastic effect on loop performance, particularly if the loop had been designed for large damping. One would conclude that the IF bandwidth is narrower than it ought to be, although possibly not narrow enough to cause serious difficulty. If ω_B is increased, the root locus will remain close to the circle for higher values of gain and the effect of the IF filter will be reduced.

In the plot shown the loop is unconditionally stable, despite the fact that damping could become very small. If the IF filter is so narrow that $\omega_B/2 < 1/\tau_2$, the loop will oscillate. The complex portion of the root locus will lie entirely in the right half plane. (If the design without IF filter is for $\zeta = 0.707$, the critical IF bandwidth will be $\omega_B/2\pi \approx 1.2\, B_L$.)

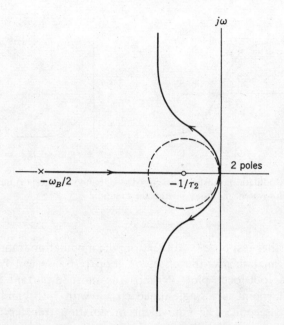

Figure 7-4   Root-locus plot showing effect of single-tuned IF filter on second-order loop.

If a second IF pole were added to the loop, the complex asymptotes of the locus would be at ± 60 degree angles to the real axis. Consequently, the locus eventually enters the right half plane and the loop oscillates.

Behavior of a third-order loop should be essentially similar to that of a second-order loop. An extra pole at $s = -\omega_B/2$ will open up the closed locus, and the complex asymptotes will be along a vertical line located at

$$s = \left(\frac{\omega_B}{2} - \frac{1}{\tau_2} - \frac{1}{\tau_4} \right)$$

τ_2 and τ_4 having been defined in Chapter 2 as the time constants of the lead terms of $F(s)$.

Oftentimes the response of the IF filter will not be known analytically;

only measured data will be available, in which case a Bode plot can be used to analyze stability.

To provide an example, Figure 7-5 shows a response scaled from actual measurements on a crystal filter. The equivalent modulation transfer response is shown in Figure 7-6 along with the Bode plot of an opened second-order loop. Bandwidth of the IF filter (3 db) is 240 radians per

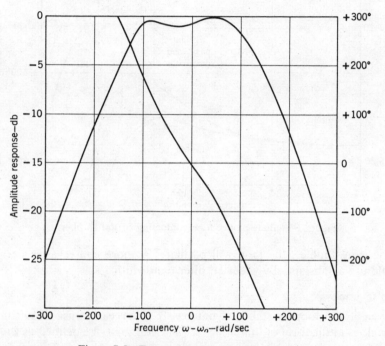

Figure 7-5   Frequency response of crystal filter.

second, whereas the loop has been arbitrarily chosen with $1/\tau_2 = 10$ rad/sec. Loop gain has been selected so that $\zeta = 0.707$. Therefore $\omega_n = \sqrt{2}/\tau_2 = 14.1$ rad/sec. (In terms of cycle bandwidth $B_L = 7.5$ Hz, and full IF bandwidth $= 38$ Hz.)

The Bode plot shows a phase margin of 30 degrees and a gain margin of 6 db. Although the loop is stable, its response will surely vary from that expected in the absence of the IF filter. If loop gain is fixed (by AGC or limiter) so that it cannot exceed the value used for the example, the stability margins are probably adequate but not ample. However, if the gain of the example is a threshold gain and increases of gain are to be expected with improved signals, the gain margin is completely inadequate.

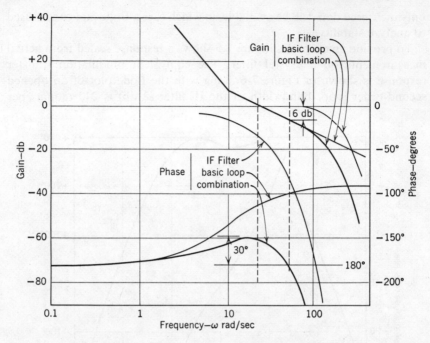

Figure 7-6   Bode plot of loop containing crystal IF filter.

If the gain doubles, the loop will oscillate. A more conservative design would use a substantially wider IF filter bandwidth.

False Lock

Even if the loop is stable, a narrow IF filter can cause acquisition difficulties in the form of "false locks." The term may be defined as those input frequencies at which the loop locks, other than the one correct lock frequency. False-lock frequencies bear no obvious relation to any of the other loop frequencies; until the source of false lock is recognized, the phenomenon when encountered can be highly disturbing and mystifying.

Previous investigations of the subject have been performed by Develet [Dev-3] and Johnson [Joh-1]. The analysis presented here follows a slightly different approach in arriving at the results.

To begin, it is instructive to return to Chapter 4 and the discussions of the lock-in and pull-in phenomena. There it is shown that phase detector output contains a small d-c component, even if the loop is not locked. We shall now derive an approximate value for that d-c component, first, in the basic loop, and then in a loop with excess phase shift arising from an IF filter. A comparison between the d-c components for these two cases will reveal the cause of false locks.

Consider an unlocked loop with input $V_s \sin \omega_i t$ and VCO output $V_o \cos \omega_o t$. Phase detector output would be $K_d \sin \Delta\omega_i t$, where $\Delta\omega_i = \omega_i - \omega_o$. (See Chapter 3 for an explanation of product-type phase detectors.)

This beat-note passes through the loop filter and frequency-modulates the VCO. In a second-order loop, if $\Delta\omega_i \gg 1/\tau_2$, the beat-note is attenuated by the filter in the ratio $\tau_2/(\tau_1 + \tau_2) \approx \tau_2/\tau_1$. (The analysis presented here is for a second-order loop, but the final results should be adaptable to any-order loop in which the loop filter has an equal number of finite zeros and poles. This includes the first-order and the most common third order loops.)

Voltage applied to the VCO is

$$\frac{K_d \tau_2}{\tau_1} \sin \Delta\omega_i t \qquad (7\text{-}1)$$

and so the frequency modulation must be

$$\frac{K_o K_d \tau_2}{\tau_1} \sin \Delta\omega_i t \qquad (7\text{-}2)$$

But (4-27) showed that

$$\frac{K_o K_d \tau_2}{\tau_1} = \Delta\omega_L \qquad (7\text{-}3)$$

which is the lock-in frequency of the second-order loop. Instantaneous frequency of the VCO is therefore

$$\omega_o + \Delta\omega_L \sin \Delta\omega_i t \qquad (7\text{-}4)$$

[Parenthetically, some additional insight into the nature of the lock-in phenomenon is gained from (7-4), which shows the VCO frequency being swept back and forth at the beat rate between the limits $\pm\Delta\omega_L$.]

Phase of the VCO is the integral of frequency; thus the VCO output voltage becomes

$$v_o(t) = V_o \cos\left(\omega_o t - \frac{\Delta\omega_L}{\Delta\omega_i} \cos \Delta\omega_i t\right) \qquad (7\text{-}5)$$

(It must be borne in mind that these expressions and the entire analysis are approximations and are valid only if $\Delta\omega_i > \Delta\omega_L$.)

Output of the phase detector is the product of the VCO voltage by the input signal or

$$v_d(t) = K_m(V_s \sin \omega_i t) V_o \cos\left(\omega_o t - \frac{\Delta\omega_L}{\Delta\omega_i} \cos \Delta\omega_i t\right) \qquad (7\text{-}6)$$

Discarding the high-frequency terms, combining V_s, V_o, and K_m into K_d

(3-3), and using trigonometric identities, we obtain the low-frequency part of the PD output as

$$K_d \sin \Delta\omega_i t \cos \left(\frac{\Delta\omega_L}{\Delta\omega_i} \cos \Delta\omega_i t \right)$$
$$+ K_d \cos \Delta\omega_i t \sin \left(\frac{\Delta\omega_L}{\Delta\omega_i} \cos \Delta\omega_i t \right) \tag{7-7}$$

The second factor of each term of (7-7) can be expanded in a Fourier series with Bessel function coefficients; that is,

$$\cos (u \cos x) = J_0(u) + 2 \sum_{k=1}^{\infty} (-1)^k J_{2k}(u) \cos 2kx \tag{7-8}$$

$$\sin (u \cos x) = 2 \sum_{k=1}^{\infty} (-1)^{k+1} J_{2k-1}(u) \cos (2k - 1)x \tag{7-9}$$

where

$$u = \frac{\Delta\omega_L}{\Delta\omega_i} \quad \text{and} \quad x = \Delta\omega_i t$$

When (7-8) and (7-9) are substituted into (7-7), it is found that the second part of (7-7) contains a term for $k = 1$ in the form of

$$2K_d \cos \Delta\omega_i t J_1 \left(\frac{\Delta\omega_L}{\Delta\omega_i} \right) \cos \Delta\omega_i t \tag{7-10}$$

which may readily be shown to have a d-c component of

$$V_d = K_d J_1 \left(\frac{\Delta\omega_L}{\Delta\omega_i} \right) \tag{7-11}$$

None of the other terms has d-c components.

This d-c is responsible for the pull-in phenomenon described in Chapter 4. Magnitude of d-c generated is shown in Figure 7-7a. For $\Delta\omega_i \gg \Delta\omega_L$ the d-c output from the phase detector is approximately

$$V_d = \frac{K_d}{2} \frac{\Delta\omega_L}{\Delta\omega_i}$$

(Richman [Ric-2] analyzes pull-in by very different methods and comes to the same asymptotic result.)

Now suppose a phase shift $\psi(\Delta\omega_i)$ is introduced into the loop, for example, by an IF filter included within the loop. The beat-note out of the phase detector becomes $K_d \sin (\Delta\omega_i t + \psi)$, and the other equations are modified as follows:

Modulating voltage is

$$\frac{K_d \tau_2}{\tau_1} \sin (\Delta\omega_i t + \psi) \tag{7-1a}$$

Frequency modulation of VCO becomes

$$\Delta\omega_L \sin (\Delta\omega_i t + \psi) \tag{7-4a}$$

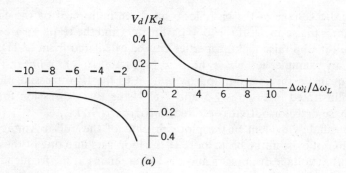

(a)

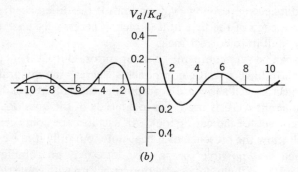

(b)

Figure 7-7 Loop pull-in characteristics showing effect of excess phase shift. (a) Basic loop only (b) Excess phase $\psi = (\pi/3)(\Delta\omega_i/\Delta\omega_L)$.

and VCO output voltage is

$$v_o(t) = V_o \cos \left[\omega_o t - \frac{\Delta\omega_L}{\Delta\omega_i} \cos (\Delta\omega_i t + \psi) \right] \tag{7-5a}$$

Low-frequency output of the PD is

$$K_d \sin \Delta\omega_i t \cos \left[\frac{\Delta\omega_L}{\Delta\omega_i} \cos (\Delta\omega_i t + \psi) \right]$$

$$+ K_d \cos \Delta\omega_i t \sin \left[\frac{\Delta\omega_L}{\Delta\omega_i} \cos (\Delta\omega_i t + \psi) \right] \tag{7-7a}$$

Once again expanding in a Fourier series with Bessel coefficients, we find that the only d-c term has a value

$$V_d = K_d J_1\left(\frac{\Delta\omega_L}{\Delta\omega_i}\right)\cos\psi(\Delta\omega_i) \qquad (7\text{-}11a)$$

The d-c voltage of the basic loop has been multiplied by the cosine of the excess phase angle. If the loop parameters and the IF phase are known, the pull-in and false-lock properties can be calculated from (7-11).

As an example, let phase be $\psi = (\pi/3)(\Delta\omega_i/\Delta\omega_L)$, a linear function of frequency; this is a fair approximation to the IF filter and phaselock loop illustrated in Figures 7-5 and 7-6. Using this expression for ψ, the d-c phase-detector output is plotted in Figure 7-7b.

Immediately evident in the plot are nulls of the pull-in voltage, nulls that do not exist in the basic loop. If the loop gets into one of these nulls, the pull-in voltage disappears and the loop remains at the frequency of the null. Actually, only the nulls with positive slope are stable; the loop will drive away from those with negative slope. (See Chapter 4, particularly Figure 4-7 and its accompanying explanation.) If the difference frequency exceeds the frequency of the first null (which is necessarily unstable), the loop will never pull in to correct lock.

A false lock can be very confusing to an operator. Output from the loop phase detector will have zero d-c component, whereas the quadrature PD (correlation detector) will show a d-c output indicating that lock has been achieved. If coherent AGC is used, the magnitude of the quad PD output is likely to be correct for indicating lock. An oscilloscope connected to the PD output will show the presence of a beat-note, but only if noise is small enough. In fact, it is possible that a false lock may go completely unrecognized—until post flight data reduction comes up with some ridiculous Doppler shift.

Obviously false locks should be avoided. One method of avoidance is to use an IF filter of sufficient bandwidth. Another is to recognize that phase shift, for a given bandwidth, increases as the number of resonant circuits in the filter increases. If only a single-tuned circuit is used, maximum phase shift is 90 degrees, and there is no finite spurious null. With two tanks (two poles in the equivalent low-pass modulation transfer function) the maximum phase shift is 180 degrees, and the only finite spurious nulls are unstable.

Rough sketches of pull-in voltage for various numbers of poles are shown in Figure 7-8. Actual false locks will be encountered only if there are four or more poles in the low-pass equivalent of the IF filter. Numerous poles are found in filters with very steep skirts—the so-called "rectangular" filters. Evidently such filters are not entirely suitable for use in a phaselock receiver.

A conservative design would utilize only one or two poles. (A single quartz crystal conveniently provides one equivalent pole.) Actually, there are certain to be other band-restricting elements within the loop, and there

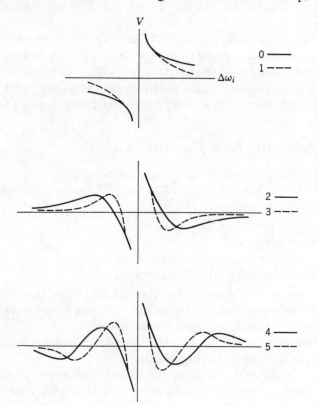

Figure 7-8 Loop pull-in characteristics. Numerals indicate equivalent number of low-pass poles in IF filter.

will always be more excess phase shift than is provided by the recognizable poles. The main IF filtering should be kept simple to provide some margin against these secondary effects, not all of which are easily predicted.

The generated d-c voltage becomes very small as $|\Delta\omega_i|$ becomes large. As a result the effective phase-detector gain, and therefore loop gain, also becomes small. This trend is reinforced by the selectivity of the IF filter which reduces the signal amplitude if $\Delta\omega_i \neq 0$. With reduced gain, the loop bandwidth will also be smaller.

It was demonstrated in Chapter 4 that the maximum trackable frequency sweep-rate depends on bandwidth; a narrow-band loop can track only a slowly varying frequency. Therefore, if acquisition is performed by sweep techniques (as is often the case), it may be possible to sweep so rapidly that the false locks will be unable to hold, but nevertheless slowly enough to succeed in acquiring correct lock. This possibility is complicated by any limiters or AGC that may be used and IF signal-to-noise ratio encountered.

From the foregoing one would conclude that the best prevention against false locks is a not-too-narrow IF filter with only a small number of poles. Unfortunately, this prescription is not always feasible, particularly if loop bandwidth is very wide. In that event it may be necessary to resort to acquisition stratagems, such as those mentioned in the preceding paragraph.

7-2   Automatic Gain Control

A receiver designer will almost always include provisions for automatic gain control (AGC) in his receiver. Among the various reasons for such practice are the following.

1. To control phaselock loop bandwidth
2. To avoid overload
3. To provide an indicator of signal level
4. To aid in providing a reliable indicator of lock

The first reason is valid only in the absence of a limiter. If, as is common, a limiter is employed, it is the limiter that controls loop bandwidth, and the AGC (in most configurations) has no effect.

Avoidance of overload is probably the most important reason and is considered in some detail in this section.

Providing signal level indication may seem to be a trivial purpose, but a level indication is often needed, and measurement of AGC control voltage is a convenient way of obtaining it.

A loop lock indication is frequently needed for proper system operation, and use of AGC may be needed to obtain a reliable indication; the reason for this statement is examined briefly in later paragraphs.

We distinguish between "coherent" and "incoherent" (also called "wideband") AGC. The incoherent automatic gain control is derived conventionally by rectifying the outpt of an IF amplifier. Rectified voltage will be proportional to the total output of the amplifier—the sum of signal, noise, and interference (if any). If noise exceeds the signal, as it may in typical phaselocked receivers, the rectified voltage will be determined primarily by the noise.

Control voltage for coherent automatic gain control is obtained from a quadrature phase detector (QPD, see Figure 4-12) in which the d-c component is proportional to signal alone. Noise will cause fluctuations in the control voltage but contribute no d-c component. By suitable filtering after the phase detector the fluctuations can be reduced to any arbitrarily small level. As a consequence, the control voltage is proportional only to the signal and is independent of noise, even if noise at the PD input greatly exceeds the signal.

Overload

To explain the overload problem it is useful to have a hypothetical, though typical, receiver as an example. A double conversion receiver is shown in simplified block form in Figure 7-9 with three AGC pickoff locations indicated. Two are incoherent and the third is coherent. Note that AGC must be generated before the limiter and not after.

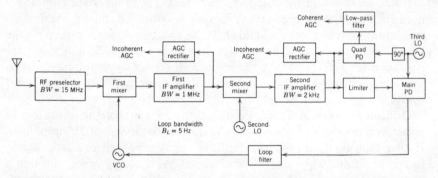
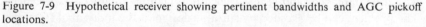

Figure 7-9   Hypothetical receiver showing pertinent bandwidths and AGC pickoff locations.

To be able to assign numbers to the example, suppose that receiver noise figure is 10 db so that receiver noise density is -194 db win a 1-cps bandwidth. Using (3-16) and assuming that the receiver threshold occurs when signal-to-noise ratio in the loop is 0 db, the threshold sensitivity is calculated to be -184 dbw. Coherent AGC can be made operative at any signal level for which the loop will lock.

At receiver threshold the output signal from the second IF amplifier will be 23 db below the noise level; from the first IF amplifier it will be 50 db below the noise level. These outputs obviously cannot provide signal-related, rectified voltages under weak signal conditions. For a wide range of useful signals conventional incoherent AGC is determined solely by noise. To obtain signal-related gain control coherent detection is essential.

We shall now examine the various sources of overload—signal, noise, and interference—one at a time. Large signals would not ordinarily be expected in normal operating circumstances, but they do occur (for example, in the launch phase of a space rocket when transmitters and receivers are separated by no more than a few miles).

If only coherent AGC is used, no AGC is generated until the receiver has acquired lock. Once lock has been obtained, the likelihood of signal overload is small, but until then it is possible that the receiver might be overloaded. To prevent strong signal overload from occurring before lock-up, designers sometimes provide two-mode AGC: both coherent and incoherent AGC detectors. Actual control would be exercised by whichever detector generated the strongest output voltage. In the unlocked condition only the incoherent detector could possibly have control, whereas the coherent detector would take over once lock had been established.

It has aready been indicated several times that limiters are commonly used in phaselocked receivers. A limiter is constantly in an overloaded condition; therefore, why should there be concern if stages preceding the limiter also overload? The answer lies in the detailed design of any particular receiver. If, in fact, the various stages act as good limiters when they are overloaded, we need not be unduly concerned with strong signal overload; the receiver would probably tolerate it.

Difficulties arise, however, because little or no thought is ordinarily given to the nature of overload behavior in the design of IF amplifiers. Rather than limit cleanly, an amplifier might very well oscillate, block, squeg, or detune when heavily overloaded. As a consequence, the signal would be damaged, and severe lock-up difficulties might be experienced. The problem can be avoided by suitable design of the individual IF stages, but it is also avoided by a two-mode AGC. Of the two solutions, the second is often the simpler.

Under conditions of very weak signal there will be no signal-caused overload, but the noise will exceed the signal, with the resulting possibility of noise overload. Of course, it is possible to design the receiver gain so that only the limiter overloads on noise and all other stages operate in a linear manner. In that case noise overload is not a problem. Nonetheless, in a conservative design it is considered good practice to build 10-to-20-db excess gain into the amplifier to provide a safety margin against deterioration of amplifier performance. With this much excess gain, the last one or two stages will almost surely overload on noise in the absence of signal or AGC.

Such overload is easily prevented by the use of incoherent AGC. We may regard the AGC as adjusting the maximum gain of the receiver just barely to avoid noise overload. Once the receiver locks to a signal, the coherent AGC further reduces over-all gain.

If the IF stages are properly designed to limit gracefully on overload, rather than to misbehave, we may very well leave out incoherent AGC and allow the overload before lock if noise overload is the only factor to be considered. Because of the small number of stages involved, there is less likely to be trouble with noise overload, compared with strong signal overload.

Next, we examine the problems of overload on interference. The potentially severe difficulties associated with co-channel interference will not be considered at all; the solution to this problem lies more in the realm of frequency allocations than in receiver design. We are concerned only with intermodulation effects caused by adjacent channel interference; that is, the interference of concern is considered to lie within the passbands of the preselector or IF amplifiers but outside the acquisition range of the phaselock loop.

Suppose that a signal has been acquired (phaselocked) and that adjacent channel interference appears. If selectivity is adequate there will be no adverse effects, provided that all stages operate linearly. The filters associated with the IF amplifiers or the phaselock loop will discriminate against the interference.

Very often, unfortunately, a strong interfering signal will overload a stage before a filter that would have eliminated the interference. In that case it is possible that intermodulation products—of which those of third order are usually the most serious—will be generated at frequencies that pass through the filters. Even if the new frequencies are outside the filter passbands, overload interference can reduce the gain and sensitivity of the receiver.

What measures can be taken to minimize the ill-effects of interference?

1. The filters should be located as far forward in the receiver as possible and should have minimum bandwidth. Selectivity should precede gain to prevent interference from entering the potentially nonlinear circuits.

2. Gain should be reduced to the minimum consistent with proper operation in the absence of interference.

3. The last requirement implies that coherent AGC should be used. If wideband AGC were employed, the gain would reach its maximum when the signal fell below the noise in the IF bandwidth. With coherent AGC, the gain does not reach maximum until nominal receiver threshold is reached.

4. Gain control should be applied as far forward as is feasible. In this

manner an interfering signal has the least opportunity of being amplified to overload before filtering.

The last rule has a number of implications worth pursuing. For one thing, it implies that gain control should immediately follow the pre-selector filter. Since a mixer is often the first element following the pre-selector, this implies that AGC should be applied to the mixer. From an interference and circuit design standpoint, this practice has much to recommend it. A diode mixer can have its conversion gain reduced by applying a d-c forward bias current; the larger the current, the smaller the gain. We may regard the current as shifting the operating point of the diode to a region of lesser curvature and therefore greater linearity. Besides gain reduction, the forward bias will improve the overload characteristics of the mixer.

Considering only the overload problem, full control of receiver gain at the mixer would be ideal; no other scheme could allow so large an inter-ference. As a practical matter, though, the range of control is limited compared with the 60- to 100-db sometimes required. An estimate of mixer gain control range might be placed at no more than 30 db. Moreover the control current will alter the RF impedance of the diode and cause mismatch and detuning of the preselector filter. (The detuning problem is discussed further in connection with gain control of IF amplifiers.)

The most serious shortcoming of mixer control is its disastrous effect on noise performance of the receiver. In many receivers the noise is primarily generated in the mixer and first IF stage. If mixer gain is controlled, it is not to be expected that the generated noise will decrease in proportion to gain. (In fact, diode shot-noise and semiconductor-noise will increase with the bias current.) Action of the AGC will be such that it will hold the receiver output signal constant; gain following the mixer remains unchanged, so that the output noise, at best, remains constant. As a consequence, the output signal-to-noise ratio can never be higher than its value at receiver threshold, which is ordinarily very poor.

What has happened, of course, is that the noise figure of the receiver has been increased at least by the same amount that mixer gain has been decreased. To preserve noise figure—and thereby allow output signal-to-noise ratio to improve with improving input—it is necessary to precede the first control element with sufficient gain. As a rough rule of thumb, we might say that the output SNR, under strong signal conditions, is not likely to exceed the gain preceding the gain-controlled element.

This rule may be derived as follows:

Suppose that the receiver consists of an amplifier with available power gain G_1 followed by an attenuator with gain $A_1 \leq 1$. Attenuator gain is dependent on signal level through action of the AGC. Noise figure of the combination is F_1, and we assume optimistically that it is constant as A_1 changes. Following the attenuator is another amplifier with gain G_2 (fixed) and noise figure F_2. The noise-power output of the receiver is

$$P_{no} = F_1 kTBG_1 A_1 G_2 + (F_2 - 1)kTBG_2$$

which is a function of the input signal power S_i because of the presence of the A_1 term. Output signal level is $S_o = S_i G_1 A_1 G_2$, which is held constant by the AGC. Attenuation A_1 must vary inversely with the signal to satisfy this equation.

At threshold we consider that $A_1 = 1$ (no attenuation) and that all noise effectively arises from the contribution of F_1. This last assumption is almost universally true in well-designed receivers. At threshold, the output signal-to-noise ratio is $S_o/P_{no} = S_o/F_1 kTBG_1 G_2$. We arbitrarily define threshold as $S_o/N_o = 1$, so that at threshold $S_o = F_1 kTBG_1 G_2$; this value remains the same for all input signals because of AGC.

For very large signals A_1 becomes extremely small. Therefore the major output noise contribution arises from F_2, in which case the output SNR becomes $S_o/P_{no} = F_1 kTBG_1 G_2/(F_2 - 1)kTBG_2 = F_1 G_1/(F_2 - 1)$, which is approximately G_1 if F_1 and F_2 are nearly equal. Q.E.D.

A number of restrictive assumptions and approximations are implicit within this rule, and it must be applied with due caution. Nonetheless, the message is clear; there is a conflict between best noise performance and best overload, and one can be improved only at the expense of the other as far as application of AGC is concerned. The optimum compromise depends on the performance requirements imposed on the receiver and the interference environment in which it must operate.

We have so far assumed that the receiver is locked to its signal and that coherent AGC is generated. Before the signal is acquired there can be no coherent AGC, and the receiver will operate at full gain. Overload interference products can then be generated within the acquisition range of the receiver (even if the interfering signals were outside the range), and the receiver can possibly lock to a phantom signal.

To reduce the chances of this or other overload troubles, it often proves useful to generate incoherent AGC whenever the receiver is out of lock. For noise, we see that, because only the second IF amplifier would be likely to overload, a two-mode AGC looks reasonable; coherent and incoherent AGC will be generated at the output of the second IF amplifier. With interference, the troubles can arise within the first IF amplifier and be completely outside the passband of the second IF. For that situation there will be no AGC generated, even incoherently, and there will be no protection against preacquisition overload.

A remedy for this ailment is three-mode control by which an AGC rectifier at the output of the first IF amplifier can take control when interference approaches the first IF overload level. Two-mode AGC has been built in presently existing equipment and has operated successfully. As far as is known, three-mode AGC has never been built, for the situations requiring it are not common.

Lock Indication

A positive indication of lock is often required in a receiver. In principle, AGC has nothing to with any lock indicator—an indication could be obtained from a quadrature phase detector operating on the same signal as the loop phase detector. In most receiver configurations, however, the signal level (without AGC) at the detector would be variable over a wide range as the input signal varied. Because output from the quadrature PD is proportional to signal, the magnitude of the lock indication voltage is highly variable.

The DC output of the QPD must be applied to some decision device that provides a "Locked" or "Unlocked" message to the outside world. Such a device is difficult to build if the decision level has a widely variable magnitude.

If coherent AGC is used, the problem disappears. Operation of the AGC is such as to maintain DC output of the QPD constant for all signals, as long as the receiver is locked. In the unlock condition, the DC output will be zero (or at least very small). A fixed decision level is entirely adequate, and no dynamic range problems develop.

The IF amplifiers driving the QPD must not overload if the level indication is to be correct. Since, in a typical receiver, the noise level will be substantially larger than a weak signal, the signal level delivered to the QPD will probably have to be fairly small, or else noise will overload the amplifier. Further amplification (DC) following the QPD and filter will often be needed.

AGC Bandwidth

Speed of response of the AGC loop is a question that has not been explored in any depth in the existing literature. For deep-space missions where signal strength changes very slowly, it has been the practice to build AGC with a very slow response [Bro-1]. Typically, the AGC noise bandwidth is much narrower than the phaselock loop bandwidth (by as much as 1000 to 1). With such a great disparity of bandwidths, noise fluctuations remaining in the AGC loop have negligible reaction on the tracking loop.

There are situations in which signal level can change rapidly and drastically. If AGC response is too slow, the receiver gain will not compensate quickly enough, and a signal reduction will appear, in effect, to be a complete dropout. As a result, the receiver will lose lock. Obviously, the AGC response must be fast enough to follow any large variations of the signal.

If AGC response is fast, its noise bandwidth must be correspondingly wide, and the receiver gain will therefore fluctuate with the noise. One would expect these gain fluctuations to have some effect on phaselock tracking, but there has been no analysis to predict the nature of the effect. Some fragmentary experimental evidence suggests that the reaction on the tracking loop is small; however, more work is needed.

A word on stability of AGC loops is also in order. If a narrow IF filter, with bandwidth comparable to the AGC loop bandwidth, is included within the AGC loop, it is entirely likely that the loop will oscillate. The problem is similar to oscillation of the tracking loop caused by the same phenomena, as explained earlier in this chapter. Furthermore, interactions between the AGC and tracking loops can be unstable, particularly if the two loop bandwidths are comparable. (This second problem does not appear to have been frequent in practice.)

Gain-Controlled Circuits

A desirable amplifier circuit would have the following properties:

1. High overload level
2. Large range of controllable gain
3. Negligible change of phase as gain is varied
4. Low noise figure

We shall see that these properties tend to be contradictory and that a compromise between them is needed. Existing device characteristics are such that a completely satisfactory compromise is rarely possible.

Power-handling capability (high overload level) can be obtained in conventional junction transistors only by operating with large collector currents. Inevitably, high currents will generate increased shot noise, and the amplifier noise figure will be degraded from its optimum value. Input stages which must have good noise performance must necessarily be inferior from an overload standpoint.

Gain of a transistor amplifier is a maximum at some optimum current and will decrease for any change of current in either direction. Gain control by a reduction in current is known as "reverse AGC," whereas control by an increase in current is known as "forward AGC." Both are capable of providing a substantial gain change. (Some transistors particularly designed for forward AGC will give a control range of 40 db in a single stage. The minimum "gain" is really a loss of 10 to 20 db.)

In a forward-controlled amplifier the power-handling capability increases as the gain is reduced with the result that overload characteristics will be as good as can reasonably be expected from a transistor. With reverse AGC, overload level drops as the gain is reduced, and at minimum gain—where the largest input signals will appear—the power-handling capability is the least. For this reason reverse AGC is regarded with considerable disfavor.

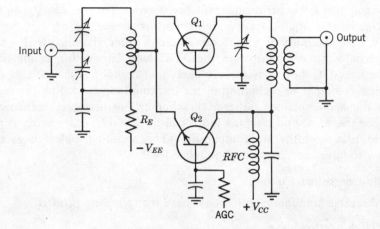

Figure 7-10   Gain-controlled amplifier which exhibits reduced phase shift.

Both conventional methods of AGC are very bad from the phase-shift standpoint. Changing the operating current of a transistor will cause a proportional change of input admittance which leads to a phase shift in the transmission of the input-coupling network. If no care is taken, severe phase changes—possibly many hundreds of degrees—will occur if several stages are controlled. Such phase changes cause serious errors in typical Doppler-tracking systems and often cannot be tolerated.

One circuit that has demonstrated reduced phase shift is shown in Figure 7-10. Two common-base transistors Q_1 and Q_2 share the same constant-current emitter supply (V_{EE} and resistor R_E). Under small signal conditions no AGC is generated, Q_2 is cut off, and Q_1 draws the entire available emitter current. For this situation Q_2 is essentially out of the circuit, and what remains is simply a grounded-base IF amplifier.

For larger signals some AGC voltage will be generated and Q_2 will begin to conduct. Any emitter current drawn by Q_2 must be robbed from Q_1, for the total available current is constant. If the input signal is regarded as coming from an RF current source, the signal current will divide between the two transistors in proportion to their individual emitter currents. As the bias current in Q_2 increases because of larger AGC voltage, more and more of the signal will be diverted into Q_2 and away from the output terminal. In principle, the active gain from input to output could be reduced to zero.

It can be shown [Gar-3] that if the variable input admittance of each transistor is proportional to the individual emitter currents (a good approximation in good transistors) and the two transistors are matched, the net input admittance presented by their paralleled emitters will remain constant, even though their relative shares of the constant emitter current supply are altered by application of AGC voltage. A major source of phase shift is thereby greatly reduced.

Casual experiment with this circuit has yielded 18-db control with less than 5 degrees phase change, and it is to be expected that further development will provide better performance. An earlier version, using a diode in place of Q_2 [Gar-3], provided 80-db gain control (over several stages) with only 5-degree phase change.

Phase changes are not completely eliminated by the two-transistor circuit; they are merely reduced. Remaining shifts are caused by an imperfect match between transistors; internal phase change, because of variation of transistor frequency response; and changes of output susceptance. These problems are reduced by close matching of the transistor pairs in d-c current transfer ratio and cutoff frequency, using very high frequency transistors, and operating into a low impedance load.

Power-handling capability is determined by the total current delivered to both emitters and is thereby constant. A large overload limit is obtained by using a large current.

Recent field-effect transistors have shown some promise of better performance than bipolar devices. Transconductance of an FET is controlled by its gate-to-source voltage. Some two-gate ("tetrode") FET's have been fabricated in which signal is applied to one gate and AGC voltage to the other. Phase shift in an FET can be caused by variation of the gate-to-channel capacitance, such variation arising from depletion region widening as reverse voltage increases. By separating signal and control gates the device transconductance can be controlled without affecting the capacitance of the signal gate. It is to be expected that, perhaps with aid of compensation techniques that have been used with vacuum tubes, excellent phase stability could be attained.

Gain control of an FET operates by bringing the device close to cutoff where its large-signal handling capability is the poorest. The relative overload capabilities of conventional transistors and FET's are not apparent, and further analysis would be of considerable value.

Voltage-controlled attenuators (VCA's) have been used in some instances. These devices often consist of forward-biased diodes acting as variable resistors. Their small-signal resistance is inversely proportional to the current through them. The diode is used as a shunt element of an attenuator in which the attenuation is varied by means of a control current.

This approach is much like forward AGC of a transistor in its toleration of large signals; it is also similar in the large susceptance changes that will occur. However, it may be feasible to build a diode with much smaller susceptance variation than a transistor and obtain less phase change. Also, it is sometimes convenient, for circuit reasons, to separate the functions of gain and gain control.

Chapter Eight

Other applications of phaselock

There are many applications of phaselock techniques besides the receivers described in Chapter 7. Discussed briefly here are tracking filters, stabilization of oscillators, frequency multipliers and dividers, frequency translation loops, discriminators, and PCM bit synchronizers. Other applications, not covered, include automatic frequency control, television synchronization, [Ric-1, 2; Sch-6, Wen-1], and automatic steering of antenna arrays [Bre-1, Bic-1].

8-1 Tracking Filters

The term "tracking filter" or "audio-tracking filter" has come to describe a phaselocked loop which is used at the output of a receiver. Thus the entire receiver is outside the loop, in contrast to the position described in Chapter 7, in which most of the receiver (beginning at the first mixer) was inside the loop.

There are some decided advantages to this tail-end approach. When phaselock was in its infancy, a separate tracking filter permitted a conventional receiver to be used without modification [Deb-1, Gar-1], as in Figure 8-1. A very weak signal (from a satellite, for example) would be added to a much stronger, fixed, local reference signal at the receiver input. The reference is required to be much stronger than any noise, so that the receiver detector will operate well above its threshold. Output of the detector is then a beat-note (in the early satellites using a 108-mc transmission frequency, the beat-note was in the audio range) between the received signal and the local reference.

The beat-note is deeply embedded in the noise, and a narrow bandwidth filter is needed to recover it. Frequency of the beat-note changes as the Doppler frequency varies, and the filter must track the beat-note frequency. A phaselock loop is an obvious and logical method of building the tracking filter.

Frequency of the local standard would be close to the expected carrier frequency of the input signal. In practice, an offset in excess of the maximum Doppler frequency is introduced so that the recovered beat-note will never pass through zero frequency.

Stability of the frequency standard is limited only by the state of the art of precision, fixed frequency oscillators and the multipliers and synthesizer needed to obtain the desired injection frequency. To a first order there need be no concern about the stability of oscillators within the receiver itself,

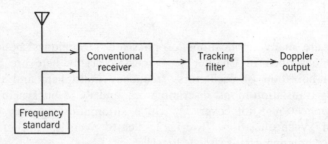

Figure 8-1   Use of tracking filter.

because any such instability will affect both signal and reference identically. The only VCO is within the tracking filter and operates at low frequencies.

It is possible to obtain much better phase stability from a fixed-frequency standard than from a VCO. Using a tail-end, tracking-filter approach, the only precision high-frequency oscillator needed may be fixed in frequency. If a phaselocked receiver is used with the entire receiver (following the first mixer) included within the loop, it is necessary to derive the first injection frequency from a VCO.

From these considerations it is sometimes possible to utilize improved oscillator stability, and therefore potentially narrower bandwidth, if a tracking-filter approach is employed.

There are, of course, disadvantages to the approach. Receiver bandwidth must exceed the entire Doppler shift that is to be accommodated. This is in contrast to the phaselocked receiver, wherein the bandwidth may be much narrower than the Doppler range and the receiver is required only to tune over the range.

Another problem develops from the inevitable change of phase shift as a function of frequency of the fixed receiver. Since input frequency will be changing, the net phase shift through the receiver changes accordingly and introduces a small error.

Considered in another manner, the shift in receiver phase from maximum

Doppler frequency to minimum appears to add additional Doppler cycles into the record. An error in velocity is necessarily incurred.

The effect can be minimized only by using wideband receivers, so that the phase change over the Doppler range will be negligible. By contrast, since a phaselocked receiver tracks the input frequency exactly, the only components contributing to a phase slope are the antenna, preselector, and any RF amplifiers. These circuits normally have large bandwidths (by comparison with a Doppler shift) and therefore usually lack significant phase slope.

8-2 Oscillator Stabilization and Clean-up

Crystal oscillators used as frequency standards have their best long-term stability if they are operated at extremely low RF power levels (crystal aging is slower at the low levels). However, as noted in Chapter 5, best short-term phase stability is obtained at an intermediate power level, where the RF signal is much greater than the circuit noise.

The best results are obtained if two separate oscillators are used: a very low-level one for good long-term stability and a second oscillator, phase locked to the first, operated at a higher level for good short-term stability. Bandwidth of the loop would be as narrow as possible, consistent with maintaining reliable lock, and output would be taken from the locked oscillator.

Using the loop is equivalent to suppressing the amplitude fluctuations of the first oscillator almost completely and passing the phase noise through an extremely narrow filter to reduce it substantially. The same technique is useful for cleaning up the output of frequency synthesizers in which harmonics and multiplier products are often present.

There is another use of phaselock in the stabilization of microwave oscillators [Ben-1, 2, 3, Bur-1, Pet-1, Poy-1, Str-1, Str-2]. A number of oscillator types (Klystrons, voltage-tuned magnetrons, BWO's and even triodes) are capable of providing moderate power outputs (50 mw to several watts) at microwave frequencies. In addition to their power capability, these devices are generally rather simple and easy to adjust but have the common drawback of poor frequency and phase stability.

To overcome the inferior stability such devices may be phaselocked to a harmonic of a stable oscillator at much lower frequency. With suitable design of the loop configuration, the harmonic power requirements can be very small—fractional microwatts,—and good locking can still be achieved.

On the assumption that the reference signal—even after repeated multiplication—has phase stability far superior* to that of the microwave oscillator, it should be clear that loop bandwidth ought to be made as wide as possible in order to obtain the best tracking and greatest reduction of phase jitter. Any low-pass loop filter will only restrict bandwidth, so that it appears reasonable to use a first-order loop with no filter at all. Bandwidth then becomes equal to loop gain K_oK_d. (Some filtering may be needed to prevent phase-detector ripple from modulating the oscillator.)

If the reference frequency can be changed, the locked oscillator may be tuned over some useful range [Pet-1, Poy-1].

8-3   Multipliers and Dividers

An oscillator can be locked to one of its harmonics or subharmonics to constitute a frequency divider or a multiplier, respectively. One application of this effect has been to obtain harmonics of a frequency standard [Cla-1]. In a related application a loop is used at the output-end of a chain of multipliers to suppress unwanted subharmonics that are difficult to remove by passive filters.

Ordinary switching-type detectors will operate only with odd harmonic relationships between input frequencies, but unusual circuits have been devised [Ped-1] so that even harmonics can also be used. Furthermore, appropriate sampling-type phase detectors [Str-3] can lock to any harmonic.

In any case, the phase detector itself may be regarded as generating harmonics of its lower-frequency input and comparing one of these with the higher-frequency input. An ideal multiplier-type phase detector generates no harmonics and therefore cannot be used in a multiplier or divider (if the inputs are sinusoidal).

For any multiplier or divider application, the lock range is ±90 degrees of the higher-frequency input. Phase-detector gain factor K_d is greatly reduced when used in harmonic service.

8-4   Translation Loops

Harmonic loops have no outstanding advantages and are not widely favored. A translation loop, on the other hand, can be extremely useful,

---

* If this assumption is not valid, there is little or no advantage to locking the microwave oscillator.

as may be seen from an example. Suppose that we wished to offset a 30-MHz signal by 1 kHz. One way to accomplish this would be by means of conventional single-sideband techniques, but good suppression of carrier and rejected sideband would depend on critical circuit adjustments.

A phaselock offset could be completely noncritical if obtained as shown in Figure 8-2. In this technique a VCO whose uncontrolled frequency is close to the desired output is heterodyned with the incoming frequency; the beat-note is close to the desired offset. This beat is compared with an oscillator whose offset frequency is exactly correct, and the loop is closed back to the VCO so that the beat-note is locked to the offset oscillator. If the input frequency is f_1 and the output is to be at $f_1 + \Delta f$, the offset oscillator must have a frequency Δf.

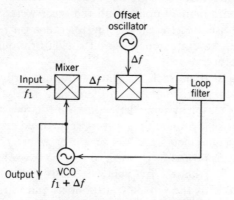

Figure 8-2   Basic translation loop.

At first appearance, it would seem that phaselock has completely eliminated the residual carrier and unwanted sidebands that remain in conventional SSB techniques. Such perfection is not obtainable in the real world; any phase-detector ripple will modulate the VCO and produce unwanted sidebands in the output. If a full-wave phase detector is used, the carrier, in principle, will not appear, and the dominant sidebands will be at $f_1 - \Delta f$ and $f_1 + 3\Delta f$. If a half-wave phase detector is used, the first-order sidebands will be at f_1 and $f_1 + 2\Delta f$; the undesired sideband at $f_1 - \Delta f$ is dependent on the second-order Bessel function. Ripple may be reduced to any desired extent by means of brute force, noncritical low-pass filtering in the loop filter. It is to be expected that such filtering will usually require a narrowing of loop bandwidth.

There is no inherent reason why the offset Δf must be obtained from a separate oscillator. Instead, it could very well be derived from f_1 by means of mixers, multipliers, and other offset loops. In this manner it is possible for the output to be coherent with the input. The following section describes coherent transponders which will be seen as a form of translation loop.

8-5 Coherent Transponders

Doppler shift of a radio signal is commonly used as a measure of the radial velocity of a moving vehicle. If one-way shift is to be determined, it is first necessary to have knowledge of the unshifted frequency of the moving transmitter. For a satellite or rocket, the maximum Doppler shift may be 20 ppm of the transmitted frequency f_t, and accuracy requirements may demand that the shift be measured with an error, from all sources, of no more than 10 ppm. If all the error were due to imperfect knowledge of transmitted frequency, the tolerance on f_t would be only five parts in 10^{11}. An exceptionally good oscillator would be needed to maintain such accuracy.

As a practical matter, such oscillators do not ordinarily leave the protected laboratory environment and are very rarely found in space vehicles. For this reason systems depending on the measurement of one-way Doppler are usually found only in very specialized applications, either where accuracy requirements are less severe or where f_t can be inferred by some means. It is far more common to rely on two-way measurements in which a signal of known frequency is transmitted from ground to vehicle, operated on by the vehicle transponder, and retransmitted to the ground at a different frequency. For Doppler measurements to have any meaning the return signal must be coherent with the up-link signal. When coherent two-way measurements are made, the requirements on oscillator accuracy are reduced by many orders of magnitude.

A transponder will be said to be coherent if its transmitted frequency f_t is a rational multiple of its received frequency f_r; that is, $f_t = (m/n)f_r$, where m and n must be integers. With this definition of coherence, there are exactly n cycles out for every m cycles that enter the transponder. The frequency received at the ground can be multiplied by n/m and the result compared against the frequency originally transmitted from the ground; their difference is the two-way Doppler shift.

High accuracy of transponder oscillators is of little concern in a two-way system; it is necessary only that the transponder be able to acquire the input signal. The ground oscillator requires a stability appropriate to the round-trip time to and from the vehicle, but the accuracy need not be extreme; one part in 10^6 is often adequate.

Earlier transponders (for example, those used for the DOVAP system) used $n = 1$; thus the output frequency was a harmonic (usually the second) of the input. A transponder of this type need not be phaselocked, although some were [Gar-3]. Our interest here is in an offset transponder in which neither m nor n is unity. The output frequency is offset—usually by a relatively small amount—from the input frequency. Coherence in offset transponders is almost always obtained by means of phaselock techniques.

A block diagram of a typical phaselocked transponder is shown in Figure 8-3. Double superheterodyne conversion is illustrated in the receiver portion, but single or triple conversion receivers operate on the

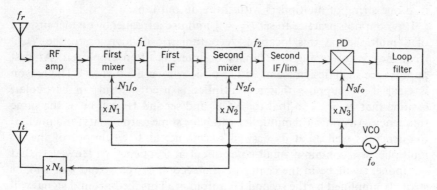

Figure 8-3   Phaselock transponder.

same principles. All mixer and phase-detector injection voltages are obtained as harmonics of a single local oscillator, and the output frequency is also a harmonic of the same oscillator. It is now shown that if the loop is locked the output will be coherent with the input.

Operation of the first mixer may be described by the equation

$$f_r = N_1 f_o \pm f_1 \tag{8-1}$$

operation of the second mixer by,

$$f_1 = N_2 f_o \pm f_2 \tag{8-2}$$

and the phaselock requirement, by

$$f_2 = N_3 f_o \tag{8-3}$$

where nomenclature is defined in Figure 8-3 and the choice of plus or minus signs depends on whether low-side or high-side injection, respectively, is used. A combination of these three equations and elimination of the two intermediate frequencies results in

$$f_r = f_0(N_1 \pm N_2 \pm N_3)$$

Because the transmitted frequency is $f_t = N_4 f_o$, the ratio of output frequency to input is

$$\frac{f_t}{f_r} = \frac{N_4}{N_1 \pm N_2 \pm N_3} \tag{8-5}$$

which is a rational number. Therefore, by our previous definition, the transponder is coherent if it is locked.

In a practical transponder the multiplication ratios will often be chosen with the result that N_1, N_2, and N_4 have many common prime factors which permit the individual frequency multipliers to be combined in substantial degree. The three individual multipliers will tend to coalesce into one string of multipliers with three output taps.

It is common practice to set $N_3 = \frac{1}{2}$ and use a frequency divider instead of a multiplier at this location. A parametric divider, or, if the VCO frequency is low enough, a binary counter, is often employed. At first appearance such design seems rather odd—why use a divider? The reason is clear if we suppose that a multiplier is used instead; in particular, assume that $N_3 = 1$, so that the VCO and second IF will be at the same frequency. Any physical multiplier will have some output at its fundamental frequency as well as at its desired harmonic, and the output of the N_2 multiplier will contain a small component at frequency f_o. However, that component will be in the center of the second IF passband and will be strongly amplified by the second IF amplifier. This feed-around signal will surely interfere with proper operation of the loop, and it is entirely possible that the loop will actually lock to itself. If we make $N_3 = \frac{1}{2}$ and provide large reverse-direction attenuation between divider and VCO, no component of the second IF will be able to loop around and cause self-lock.

The intermediate frequencies are not fixed; instead, they vary as the input frequency varies, although over smaller limits. Phase slope of the IF filters must be small enough so that the changing frequency will not produce a significant Doppler error.

8-6 Discriminators

Phaselock loops are widely used as frequency discriminators for FM-FM telemetry. In this service they provide a somewhat improved threshold over conventional discriminators but can be troublesome if they drop out of lock.

To understand operation of a loop as a discriminator it is useful to begin with the phase-error response (2-7).

$$\theta_e(s) = [1 - H(s)]\,\theta_i(s) = \frac{s\theta_i(s)}{s + K_o K_d\, F(s)}$$

As a practical matter, attention is restricted to the passive-filter, second-order loop. For that case (2-7) becomes

$$\theta_e(s) = \frac{[s(\tau_1 + \tau_2) + 1]\,s\theta_i(s)}{[s^2(\tau_1 + \tau_2) + s(1 + K_oK_d\tau_2) + K_oK_d]} \tag{8-6}$$

and the phase detector output voltage is $V_d = K_d\theta_e$.

The term $s\theta_i(s)$ in (8-6) represents the frequency modulation of the input signal; output voltage from the phase detector therefore is recovered modulation, filtered by the bracketed terms.

Direct use of the phase-detector output is unsatisfactory for two reasons: the output would be noisy and the equivalent filter undesirable. The noise difficulty may be appreciated from inspection of Figure 2-4, from

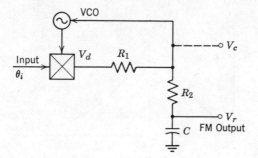

Figure 8-4   Loop used as discriminator.

which it can be seen that nearly all of the input noise will appear at the phase-detector output.

These difficulties are circumvented by taking the demodulated signal from the output of the loop filter (V_r in Figure 8-4).* It is readily determined that

$$\frac{V_r}{V_d} = [s(\tau_1 + \tau_2) + 1]^{-1} \tag{8-7}$$

so that the output voltage is

$$
\begin{aligned}
V_r &= \frac{s\theta_i(s)K_d}{s^2(\tau_1 + \tau_2) + s(1 + K_oK_d\tau_2) + K_oK_d} \\
&= \frac{K_ds\theta_i(s)/(\tau_1 + \tau_2)}{s^2 + s(1 + K_oK_d\tau_2)/(\tau_1 + \tau_2) + K_oK_d/(\tau_1 + \tau_2)} \\
&= s\theta_i(s)\left(\frac{1}{K_o}\right)\frac{\omega_n^2}{s^2 + 2\zeta\omega_ns + \omega_n^2} \tag{8-8}
\end{aligned}
$$

* Sometimes the VCO control voltage (V_c in Figure 8-4) is used as the FM output, in which case an RC filter (with time constant R_2C) should be used to obtain the best filtering. However, the external filter is superfluous if the output is V_r.

The first factor of this product, $s\,\theta_i(s)$, is the frequency modulation of the input signal, the second term is a gain factor, and the third term represents a second-order, low-pass filter.

(It is common practice to employ a postdetection filter after the discriminator; five- and six-pole Butterworth and Bessel characteristics are frequently encountered. The two-pole filtering of the loop is conveniently incorporated into the total postdetection filter, thereby reducing the complexity of the external filter. For the remainder of this discussion the existence of external postfiltering is not considered.)

Noise spectrum at the FM output is also described by (8-8). Input phase noise is typically white, and the shape of the noise power spectrum

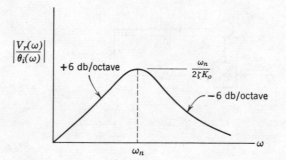

Figure 8-5   Discriminator phase-noise transfer function.

is the same as the squared magnitude of the transfer function; that is, $|V_r(\omega)/\theta_i(\omega)|^2$. The transfer function has the familiar triangular shape associated with the output noise spectrum of conventional FM detectors (see sketch in Figure 8-5).

Equation 8-8 is obtained on the basis of a linear approximation to the phase-detector characteristic. Linearity is very important in a discriminator, for any nonlinearity will probably be interpreted as data error. In order to obtain good linearity it is common practice to make use of the triangular-characteristic phase detector (Figure 5-7b), which is linear in the range of ± 90 degrees. By contrast, a sinusoidal characteristic departs from a straight line by almost 5 percent at ± 30 degrees. Useful range of the triangular detector is therefore almost tripled.

A triangular characteristic is obtained by applying square waves to both inputs of the phase detector. A limiter may be used to obtain a square waveform from a sinusoidal signal.

The behavior of a bandpass limiter is described in Chapter 5. A bandpass limiter has a filter in its output that suppresses all harmonics, but the limiter used ahead of a phaselocked discriminator cannot have such a filter if a square wave is to be delivered to the phase detector. All the properties of the bandpass limiter are based on the use of an output filter. If the filter is absent, there is no assurance that the properties will remain unchanged or even similar. Nevertheless, for lack of better information (no analysis of the wideband limiter could be found), it is *assumed* that the wideband limiter has the properties outlined in Chapter 5.

When a limiter is used, the signal suppression factor α must be taken into account at low signal-to-noise ratios. In (8-8) natural frequency ω_n and damping ζ are both dependent on α. The filtering action (loop bandwidth) is a function of SNR. Bandwidth (ω_n) reduction is 3 percent at $(\text{SNR})_i$ of $+10$ db and 18 percent at 0 db (5-4).

Gilchriest [Gil-1] points out that this suppression effect also exists in conventional discriminators. However, in that case the bandwidth is fixed, but the gain of the discriminator is reduced. Therefore, if the discriminator is calibrated at high SNR, it will be out of calibration at low SNR. Gain will be proportional to α and is therefore reduced by 6 percent at the $+10$-db threshold SNR of conventional discriminators. A phaselock discriminator exhibits this change of calibration only to the extent that the change of bandwidth affects the signal; d-c calibration remains unchanged.

(Ordinarily, no effort is expended to compensate for the change in loop bandwidth. However, coherent AGC, derived and applied after the limiter, would appear to offer a method of keeping bandwidth constant. No mechanization of this idea has come to light in the literature.)

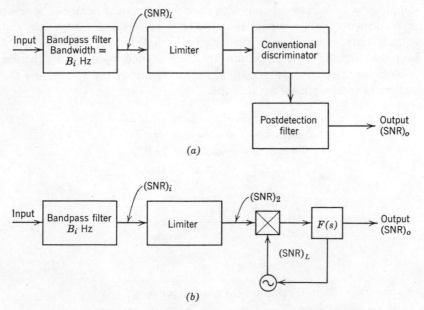

Figure 8-6   Discriminator configurations. (*a*) Conventional (*b*) Phaselocked.

Above threshold a phaselocked discriminator has an output SNR identical to that of a conventional discriminator with the same input and output filtering. Threshold of a conventional discriminator is considered to be $+10$-db SNR at the input to the limiter; we shall derive approximate threshold values for the phaselock loop in order to determine the improvement that can be gained.

The block diagrams of Figure 8-6 apply to the analysis. Comparisons between thresholds are based on $(SNR)_i$, the signal-to-noise ratio in the input bandwidth B_i. This is also the signal-to-noise ratio applied to the limiter.

Determination of phaselock discriminator threshold proceeds as follows:

1. Specify modulation characteristics.
2. Determine input bandwidth (B_i) requirements from modulation parameters.
3. Determine loop bandwidth needed to accommodate modulation.
4. Estimate loop threshold $(SNR)_{LT}$ (see Chapter 3).
5. Calculate signal-to-noise ratio at input to loop as

$$(SNR)_{2T} = \frac{2B_L}{B_i}(SNR)_{LT} \qquad (8\text{-}9)$$

6. Adjust for effect of limiter (Figure 5-1 and Equation 5-3) to obtain threshold signal-to-noise ratio $(SNR)_{iT}$ at the input to the limiter.

The first type of modulation to be analyzed is a full-bandwidth frequency step, $\Delta\omega = 2\pi B_i$. Loop bandwidth is selected to yield peak phase error of 90 degrees. (It is assumed that the loop has relatively high gain and that the static error is much smaller.) Peak phase error may be obtained from the curves of Figure 4-3 and minimum ω_n determined as a function of damping. Loop bandwidth B_L is then calculated from (3-12), and the numerical results are shown in Table 8-1.

Table 8-1 Minimum Allowable Loop Bandwidth B_L for Frequency Step $\Delta\omega = 2\pi B_i$

ζ	B_L/B_i
0.5	1.08
0.707	0.98
1	0.93
2	0.89
5	1.01

Peak transient phase error $= 90°$

From this table it can be seen that we may take loop-noise bandwidth B_L as being equal to input bandwidth B_i for any practical value of damping. Maximum error incurred by this approximation is no more than $\frac{1}{2}$ db. The need for loop bandwidth equal to input bandwidth must be regarded with caution and some scepticism with respect to final results. In Chapter 3, in which noise performance of a loop was first analyzed, the approximation $B_i \gg B_L$ was made. It is not clear that this approximation can be disregarded with impunity.

Somewhat arbitrarily and very optimistically, we select the definition of loop threshold as 0 db; that is $(SNR)_{LT} = 1$, which leads to $(SNR)_{2T} = 2$ from (8-9). Using Figure 5-1, we find that the input threshold is approximately

$$\boxed{SNR_{iT} = 1.4 \text{ (about 1.5 db)}} \qquad (8\text{-}10)$$

Therefore, if the input modulation is a full-bandwidth frequency step, the threshold improvement over a conventional discriminator is computed to be in the neighborhood of 8.5 db.

In actual practice this predicted improvement seems to be overly optimistic—by perhaps as much as 6 db. A better analysis and some firm experimental evidence are badly needed.

A full-bandwidth step input is a rather drastic requirement to impose on a loop. A discriminator must accommodate the step if PAM-FM-FM is the modulation form, but if ordinary FM-FM is used the situation changes, and a narrower loop bandwidth is allowable.

Consider that sinusoidal frequency modulation with deviation $\Delta\omega$ and maximum modulating frequency ω_m has been applied to the incoming signal. Modulation index is $\Delta\omega/\omega_m$ and is denoted by the symbol D. According to Black,* the RF bandwidth occupied by an FM signal is effectively $2(\Delta\omega + \omega_m) = 2(D + 1)\omega_m$. We assume that the bandwidth $2\pi B_i$ of the input filter is set equal to this minimum permissible bandwidth. Using this assumption, we find that it is possible to determine $\Delta\omega$ and ω_m if D and B_i are specified.

Equation 4-12 gives the loop phase error for sinusoidal FM input. From this equation we determine the value of ω_n that causes the peak error to be 90 degrees; this value defines the minimum allowable bandwidth of the loop. In terms of D and B_i (rather than $\Delta\omega$ and ω_m), the minimum natural frequency can be shown to be

$$\omega_{n_{min}} = \frac{\pi B_i}{D + 1}\left[1 - 2\zeta^2 + \sqrt{(1 - 2\zeta^2)^2 + 1 + 4D^2/\pi^2}\right]^{\frac{1}{2}} \qquad (8\text{-}11)$$

* H. S. Black, *Modulation Theory*, Van Nostrand, New York, 1953.

where it has been assumed that loop gain is large. (To be precise, $\Delta\omega/K_oK_d \ll \pi/2$. If this assumption is incorrect, a wider bandwidth is needed.)

If damping and natural frequency are known, loop-noise bandwidth may be calculated from (3-12). Figure 8-7 shows plots of minimum noise bandwidth versus modulation index for different values of damping. (The results for small modulation index should be regarded with suspicion, for $B_L > B_i$ for that case.)

It may be seen from the figure that, if $D > 5$, damping of $\zeta = 0.5$ permits the smallest bandwidth. (This finding is in harmony with Spilker's

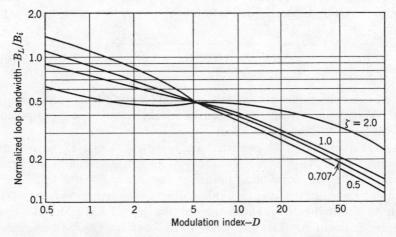

Figure 8-7   Minimum loop bandwidth for sinusoidal FM.

[Spi-3] conclusion that $\zeta = 0.5$ is optimum for large modulation indices.) For small D it is evident that heavy damping is needed if a small bandwidth is to be obtained.

We must next arrive at a specification for loop threshold. The easy-to-choose level of 0 db is overly optimistic; presence of modulation must be taken into account by some means. There is no rigorous method of defining loop threshold (see Chapter 3) and a heuristic argument of some kind is needed. Consider the following argument:

Tracking of modulation is necessarily imperfect, and a sinusoidal error with peak amplitude ϕ occurs. Now, change the frame of reference of frequency from a fixed frequency to the variable instantaneous frequency of the VCO. In this new frame of reference the loop appears as a fixed filter with an input signal angle-modulated sinusoidally to a peak index of ϕ radians. "Carrier" amplitude of this modified input is proportional to the zero-order Bessel function $J_o(\phi)$.

At this point we make the assumptions needed to specify a threshold:

1. Only the virtual carrier, as seen in the variable frequency reference frame, is effective in holding lock; that is, we assume that the power in the virtual sidebands is wasted, at least for tracking purposes.

2. In the absence of modulation, loop threshold is taken to be 0 db (see Chapter 3).

Using these two assumptions, we find that the loop threshold is

$$(\text{SNR})_{LT} = [J_o(\phi)]^{-2} = 4.62 \text{ or } +6.6 \text{ db} \qquad (8\text{-}12)$$

for $\phi = 90°$.

Threshold signal-to-noise ratio at the phase detector may be obtained from (8-9) and (8-12) as $(\text{SNR})_{2T} = 9.24 \, B_L/B_i$. Bandwidth ratio may be

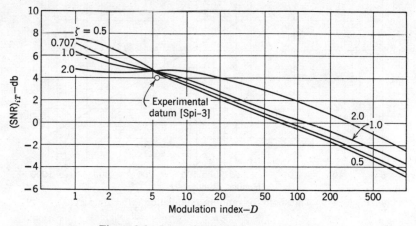

Figure 8-8   Input threshold for sinusoidal FM.

obtained from Figure 8-7, and adjustment for the effect of the limiter can be done by using Figure 5-1. The resulting input threshold is plotted in Figure 8-8 as a function of modulation index and loop damping.

Spilker [Spi-3] has analyzed the same problem (phaselock discriminator with sinusoidal modulation) by using a substantially different technique and different assumptions to specify threshold. Nevertheless, his results are very close to those derived here. Also, he performed laboratory measurements and obtained one experimental datum point, as shown in Figure 8-8. The agreement between measurement and calculation is quite good and indicates that the method of analysis is not far wrong. The following conclusions may be drawn from Figure 8-8:

1. There is always some threshold improvement over the +10 db of a conventional discriminator.

2. Improvement is greatest for large modulation index.

3. If modulation index is large, a damping of $\zeta = 0.5$ appears optimum.
4. If modulation index is small, the loop should be heavily damped.
5. For $D \approx 5$ the threshold is virtually independent of ζ. The IRIG FM-FM standard is $D = 5$; therefore the common practice of utilizing the two poles of the loop as part of a more complex postdetection filter has no adverse effect on threshold.

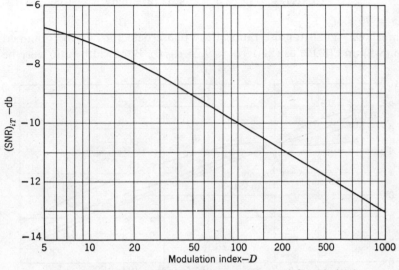

Figure 8-9   Threshold for random modulation (after Lindsey).

Modulation spectrum is another item to consider. A step input occurs if PAM or PDM data are to be handled, but sinusoidal modulation is usually only a convenient fiction. Lindsey [Lin-1] has considered the case in which the modulation is equivalent to white noise passed through a simple RC filter with a transfer function of $\omega_m/(s + \omega_m)$. If we still define modulation index as $D = \Delta\omega/\omega_m$, it is still reasonable to require $2\pi B_i = 2(D + 1)\omega_m$ as the minimum bandwidth of the input filter.

Lindsey computes input threshold by using the criterion of total rms error equal to 1 radian as the definition of loop threshold. His results* are plotted in Figure 8-9. (There is no indication of damping because the Wiener optimum filter has been used for each modulation index.) It is evident that a filtered random modulation is not so severe a constraint as sine wave FM, for Lindsey's threshold is some 8 to 12 db less than the

* In a later article [Lin-3] he points out that threshold is strongly dependent on modulation spectrum and that suitable premodulation filtering can enhance system performance in considerable degree.

best in Figure 8-8. (Remember, however, that D and ω_m have different meanings in the two figures.)

The following conclusions may be drawn regarding discriminators:

1. At high input SNR's there is no appreciable difference between phaselocked and conventional types.

2. A phaselocked loop will have a lower threshold than the $+10$ db of a conventional discriminator.

3. The improvement that can be gained depends on the modulation of the input signal. No one number or one rule will cover all situations.

4. Even when modulation has been specified, there is still some uncertainty over the obtainable improvement because of the arbitrariness of any definition of phaselock threshold.

5. For best results the loop should be specifically designed for the modulation actually present.

6. Premodulation filtering can provide better performance.

8-7 PCM Bit Synchronization

A PCM signal consists of a series of binary digits (bits) occurring at a periodic rate. The weight of each bit ("zero" or "one") is random but the duration of each bit, and therefore the periodic "bit rate," is constant (or essentially so). For detection and further processing of the digits it is necessary to have a "clock" that is coherent with the bit rate. This clock must ordinarily be derived from the incoming data stream.* Phaselock techniques are widely used to recover the clock from the data.

Some form of Nonreturn to Zero (NRZ) modulation is almost always used to maximize data rate in a given transmission bandwidth. In a truly random NRZ bit stream there are no discrete frequency components present; specificially, there is no component at the bit rate.† In fact, the continuous spectrum of an NRZ wave has a null at the bit frequency.

A helpful analogy is found in double-sideband, suppressed-carrier modulation. In this case the carrier is not present (it has been balanced out at the modulator), but a local carrier is needed for proper demodulation. It has been demonstrated [Cos-1] that a DSB signal has sufficient information in the sidebands to permit carrier reconstruction at the receiver. A modified form of phaselock is used for the reconstruction.

---

* Sometimes a separate pilot signal is transmitted for synchronization purposes. This is rare and contrary to IRIG PCM standards. Moreover, Stiffler [Sti-1] has shown that the best use of transmitter power is obtained by devoting all power to the data and none to a pilot.

† W. R. Bennett, "Statistics of Regenerative Digital Transmission," *BSTJ*, Vol. 37, pp. 1501–1542, November 1958.

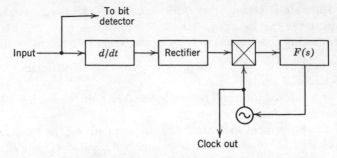

Figure 8-10   Timing recovery for NRZ digital data.

Similarly, an NRZ signal may be regarded as lacking a "carrier" which must be reconstructed from information contained within the signal. It is impossible to recover the clock merely by applying the input signal to the phaselock loop; there is nothing on which the loop can lock.

Timing information in a PCM signal is carried in the data transitions; the time of a transition marks one boundary of an individual bit. Transitions can have either positive or negative direction, but both polarities have the same meaning for timing recovery. If a series of unidirectional pulses is generated to mark transition times, there will be a discrete component of the bit frequency in the pulse train and a loop can be locked to it.

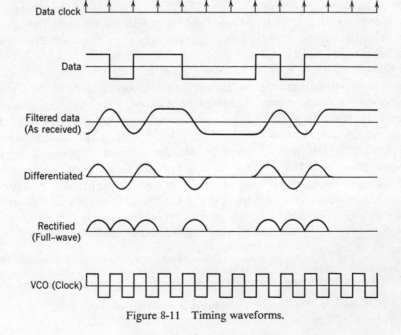

Figure 8-11   Timing waveforms.

Figure 8-10 illustrates one method of timing recovery. Figure 8-11 shows typical waveforms. In this illustration, pretransmission filtering of the bit stream has been assumed. The received signal is first differentiated to mark the locations of the data transitions. A rounded pulse of corresponding polarity is obtained for each positive and negative transition.

A rectifier converts all pulses to the same polarity. A full-wave rectifier has been shown, but half-wave is possible. On the average, half the available information is discarded by a half-wave rectifier.

The rectified pulses can be shown to contain a discrete spectral component at the bit frequency that the loop can track. For convenience of understanding, the rectifier output may be considered to be a coherent signal, periodic at the bit rate, that is randomly keyed on and off by a keying signal whose transitions are synchronous with the bit rate. During the "on" intervals the loop tracks the coherent signal; during the "off" intervals the loop remembers the last frequency present and still provides a clock output.

The apparatus of Figure 8-10 can and has been used as shown. There are other methods (such as variations of early-late gates) that are also encountered frequently. Whatever the actual details may be, all systems must have the following two properties in common:

1. A method of locating the data transitions. This is normally performed by some kind of linear differentiating or differencing operation.

2. A form of rectification that converts the transition information to a usable form. This operation is necessarily a second-order (or higher even-order) nonlinearity.

Chapter Nine

Testing the phaselock loop

Measurement of loop characteristics can be troublesome, particularly if approached in a straightforward manner. Many of the parameters to be measured [e.g., $H(j\omega)$ the phase transfer function] are somewhat unusual and may require special test equipment. Bandwidths are likely to be very narrow, thereby requiring that signal generators be exceptionally stable and well calibrated. Loops operate on a signal deeply immersed in noise, and measurements generally become difficult when noise is present. Finally, many loop characteristics are dependent on signal level and/or signal-to-noise ratio.

Various measurement techniques are presented in the following pages. Emphasis is placed on expedients by which the difficulties mentioned above can be avoided or minimized.

9-1 Static Measurements

A stable cw signal generator is nearly indispendable for most loop measurements, and the availability of such an instrument is assumed for all of the techniques considered. If the signal generator is tunable and well calibrated, it is a simple matter to obtain phase-error voltage (d-c output of phase detector) as a function of input frequency in a locked loop.

From Chapter 4 it will be recalled that the static phase-error is

$$\theta_v = \frac{\Delta\omega}{K_v} = \frac{2\pi\,\Delta f}{K_o K_d\,F(0)} \tag{9-1}$$

Output of the phase detector is $K_d\theta$, and the measured d-c output is

$$V_d = \frac{2\pi\,\Delta f}{K_o\,F(0)} \tag{9-2}$$

These measurements provide the value of $K_o\,F(0)$. More significantly,

120

the hold-in range and the shape of the phase-detector characteristic (over the hold-in range) can be determined. Hold-in range is easily measured as the two extremes of mistuning over which lock is maintained.

The plot of phase-error voltage versus input frequency reveals the dominant nonlinearities of the loop. If the VCO and d-c amplifiers (if any) do not saturate, the curve obtained will indicate the shape of the phase-detector characteristic. However, if a high-gain d-c amplifier is used, the dominant nonlinearity is likely to be saturation of the amplifier. Hold-in range is then limited by saturation level, and as a consequence phase-error voltage versus frequency curve is likely to be linear over the full hold-in range.

It will sometimes happen that no variable-frequency signal generator available has adequate stability for a narrow-band loop to be able to

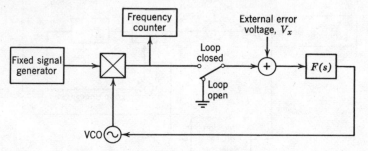

Figure 9-1   Static self-check of phaselock loop.

lock to it. In that case a fixed-frequency crystal oscillator will often be built to supply a usable input signal, thereby sacrificing the convenience of variable input frequency.

To be able to perform variable-frequency measurements, it is necessary only to be able to introduce an external error voltage into the loop and to measure the frequency of phase-detector beat-notes. A possible arrangement is shown in Figure 9-1.

A switch is used to open and close the loop, and a summing network adds V_x to the phase-detector output. When the loop is open, there is a frequency difference between the signal generator and VCO; the result is a beat-note from the phase detector. The frequency counter measures the frequency difference.

Unlocked frequency of the VCO depends on the external error voltage; it is necessary for the phase detector to generate a voltage opposing V_x in order to bring the loop into lock.

A plot of VCO offset frequency versus V_d provides exactly the same information obtained by varying the input frequency. Determination of

$F(0)K_0$ is possible without even closing the loop. Hold-in range and phase-detector characteristic shape (or other loop nonlinearity) measurements require the loop first to be opened (to measure frequency) and then closed* (to verify locking and to measure phase-error voltage, V_d) for each point tested.

The measurements described so far make use of the loop phase detector as part of the measurement instrumentation. In order to measure phase error per se or d-c loop gain, $K_v = K_d K_0 F(0)$, it is necessary to calibrate the phase-detector gain factor K_d. Inasmuch as K_d is likely to be dependent

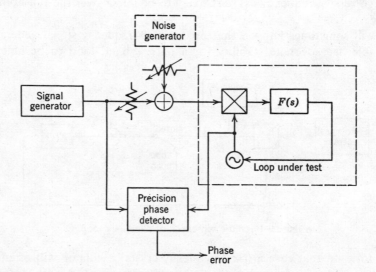

Figure 9-2   Measurement of phase error.

on signal level and/or signal-to-noise ratio, calibration can be quite inconvenient; an independent method of phase-error measurement would often be desirable.

One technique of phase measurement is illustrated in Figure 9-2. An instrumentation phase detector is used to measure phase difference between the input signal and VCO. Inputs to this phase detector are at a fixed level (note the location of the attenuators in Figure 9-2), and both inputs are essentially free of noise. Therefore calibration of the precision phase detector is fixed and does not depend on signal level or signal-to-noise

* If frequency offset exceeds lock-in range, it may require an excessive time for pull-in to occur when the loop is closed. A convenient way to avoid such difficulty might be to reduce V_x to zero each time the loop is closed, obtain rapid lock, and then increase V_x to the desired test value. Corresponding frequency offset would then be determined by opening the loop and letting V_x remain unchanged.

ratio at the loop input. Direct measurement of phase error thereby becomes feasible.

Because both inputs to the measuring phase detector are essentially noise-free, a flip-flop type detector with sawtooth characteristic can be used, provided frequency is not too high. The sawtooth, of course, has the advantage of excellent linearity over a phase range of 360 degrees.

Use of an external phase detector is extremely complicated if, as often happens, the input signal and VCO are not at the same frequency. (One example would be a phaselocked superheterodyne receiver.) To be able to use the external phase detector it is necessary to perform a coherent translation of the signal generator frequency to the VCO frequency and to use the translated signal as one input of the phase detector. Such a translator can prove to be a relatively complex item of equipment, but in any event it is a special purpose instrument that probably would have to be custom-built for each particular application.

9-2 Acquisition

Lock-in and pull-in limits can be determined with a variable-frequency signal generator if a lock indication of some kind is available (see Chapter 4). To measure acquisition performance the input signal is removed and the VCO allowed to settle to its free-running frequency. The signal generator frequency is then offset from that of the VCO and the signal reapplied to the input.

If the loop eventually locks up, the frequency offset was within pull-in range. If lock occurs without any slipping of cycles, the offset was within lock-in range. The distinction between lock-in and pull-in might become rather blurred in a practical case, particularly if appreciable noise is encountered.* Rather than concern oneself with the distinction, it may be more useful to determine capture range and capture time. Capture range, of course, is identical to pull-in range. Capture time is obtained by measuring the time between the application of an offset signal (as already described) and the achievement of lock. In the presence of noise, capture time will exhibit statistical fluctuations, and many trials are needed to obtain a meaningful average.

Sweep acquisition measurements are conceptually less difficult. Ordinarily, the sweep circuits will have been built into the loop under test; consequently, a fixed-frequency signal generator, a lock indicator, and

---

* Instrumentation of cycle slippage is not easy. Signal-to-noise ratio at the input must be high enough that the beat-note out of the phase detector can be readily discernible above the noise. Also, the lock-up transient is probably much too fast to be seen on an oscilloscope; a permanent record on an oscillograph is needed.

perhaps a noise generator are the only instruments needed. Sweep rate, sweep excursion, signal-to-noise ratio, and loop bandwidth would all be regarded as variables, and success or failure of acquisition would be determined for assorted conditions of interest. It must be remembered that success of acquisition is a statistical quantity (see Chapter 4), particularly with noise present, and repeated trials are needed. The quantity eventually determined is probability of successful acquisition for the various conditions.

9-3   Dynamic Measurements

Under this heading we include transient response and sinusoidal frequency response.

Frequency Response

A brute force method of determining frequency response [transfer function of phase $H(j\omega)$ from input signal to VCO output] would utilize the phase-modulated signal generator and phase detector illustrated in Figure 9-3. Such instrumentation would undoubtedly work—if it were available. However, phase-modulated signal generators are not widely manufactured, and it is highly unlikely that most laboratories would possess one. Alternative methods are to be preferred.

One alternative is to utilize a frequency-modulated signal generator

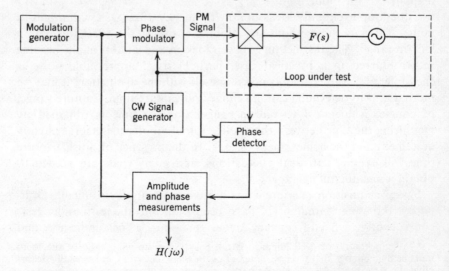

Figure 9-3   Frequency response measurement using PM signal generator.

(a more common laboratory instrument) and the test setup illustrated in Figure 9-4. Principles of operation of this arrangement are derived as follows:

From (2-7) the loop phase error $\theta_e(s)$ due to input phase modulation $\theta_i(s)$ is

$$\theta_e(s) = \frac{s\,\theta_i(s)}{s + K_o K_d\,F(s)}$$

Output of the phase detector is $K_d\,\theta_e(s)$, and output of the loop filter is $F(s)K_d\,\theta_e(s)$; therefore the output shown in Figure 9-4 is

$$V_2(s) = \frac{s\,\theta_i(s)K_d\,F(s)}{s + K_o K_d\,F(s)} \tag{9-3}$$

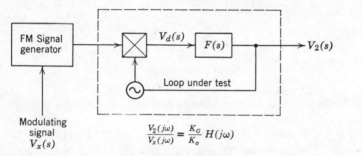

$$\frac{V_2(j\omega)}{V_x(j\omega)} = \frac{K_G}{K_o}\,H(j\omega)$$

Figure 9-4   Frequency response measurement using FM signal generator.

By making use of (2-6) we find that this expression may be written as

$$V_2(s) = \frac{s\,\theta_i(s)}{K_o}\,H(s) \tag{9-4}$$

The factor $s\,\theta_i(s)$ will be recognized as the frequency modulation of the input RF signal. Moreover, instantaneous frequency deviation is $v_x(t)K_G$ (where K_G is modulator sensitivity in radians per second per volt), and $s\,\theta_i(s) = K_G\,V_x(s)$. By using this fact and substituting $s = j\omega$ we have

$$\frac{V_2(j\omega)}{V_x(j\omega)} = \frac{K_G}{K_o}\,H(j\omega) \tag{9-5}$$

In other words, the technique determines frequency response to within an arbitrary gain constant. Because it is known that $H(j0) = 1$, the value of gain constant is unimportant; only the shape of $H(j\omega)$ is needed.

If loop bandwidth is narrow, it is necessary to use very low modulating frequencies for the response test. Unfortunately, many commercial FM signal generators have capacitively coupled modulation inputs, with cutoff frequencies in the region of 5 to 10 Hz. Such an instrument is incapable of accepting the low modulating frequencies that might be needed—perhaps 0.1 Hz or lower in a vary narrow loop. Moreover, the short-term stability of commercial equipment is not likely to be adequate to permit locking by a narrow-band loop.

The solution to this problem is the same used for static measurements: a fixed-frequency, stable-signal generator combined with the introduction of modulation into the loop itself. Figure 9-5 shows the test arrangement.

As before, $\theta_o(s) = K_o\, V_2(s)/s$ [from (2-5)] and $V_d(s) = K_d[\theta_i(s) - \theta_o(s)]$.

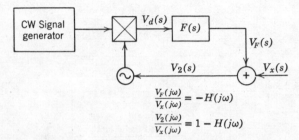

$$\frac{V_F(j\omega)}{V_x(j\omega)} = -H(j\omega)$$

$$\frac{V_2(j\omega)}{V_x(j\omega)} = 1 - H(j\omega)$$

Figure 9-5   Frequency response measurement using internal modulation.

Input signal is unmodulated, and its phase can be accepted as the system reference. Therefore we can arbitrarily set $\theta_i = 0$, which leaves $V_d(s) = -K_d\,\theta_0(s)$. Furthermore, $V_F(s) = F(s)\, V_d(s)$, and $V_2(s) = V_F(s) + V_x(s)$.

Combination of these relations leads to

$$V_F(s) = \frac{-K_o K_d\, F(s)\, V_x(s)}{s + K_o K_d\, F(s)} \tag{9-6}$$

Use of (2-6) and $s = j\omega$ leads to

$$\frac{V_F(j\omega)}{V_x(j\omega)} = -H(j\omega) \tag{9-7}$$

which is the phase-transfer function, except for an unimportant sign reversal. By using this technique we need only a crystal oscillator and standard audio (and subaudio) laboratory test instruments. Requirements for special equipment are minimal.

Error response is also obtainable. From (2-7) $\theta_e(s) = \theta_i(s)\,[1 - H(s)]$. In Figure 9-5, $V_2 = V_F + V_x$, whereas (9-7) shows $V_F = -H(j\omega)V_x$, so that

$$\frac{V_2(j\omega)}{V_x(j\omega)} = 1 - H(j\omega) \tag{9-8}$$

which is the phase-error response.

In a second-order loop the response is completely known, in principle, if the two parameters ζ and ω_n are known. If these two parameters can be measured by simple techniques, the necessity for complete response measurements is reduced.

(There are two sides to this argument. On the one hand, the quantities of prime interest are ζ and ω_n; it is decidedly inconvenient to try to infer them from plots of $|H(j\omega)|$ (see Figure 2-3). On the other hand, parasitic elements in the loop—such as IF amplifiers—will alter the response from that of the ideal second-order system. This alteration is likely to be most significant in the high-frequency skirts of the response. A measurement of the response is needed to reveal the existence and magnitude of such an effect. Therefore it will often be true that both simplified and complete measurements will be needed.)

In the test setup of Figure 9-4 suppose that the output voltage V_d from the phase detector is measured, rather than V_2 as before. By operations similar to those that have gone before it can be shown that

$$\frac{V_d(s)}{V_x(s)} = K_G K_d [s + K_o K_d\, F(s)]^{-1} \qquad (9\text{-}9a)$$

In like manner, in Figure 9-5, the phase-detector output is related to test voltage V_x by

$$\frac{V_d(s)}{V_x(s)} = -K_o K_d [s + K_o K_d\, F(s)]^{-1} \qquad (9\text{-}9b)$$

Both expressions contain the same bracketed term $[s + K_o K_d\, F(s)]^{-1}$; this is the transfer function of phase error due to input frequency modulation. Amplitude of sinusoidal response response for a high-gain, second-order loop is plotted in Figure 4-1.* It may be seen that response peaks at $\omega = \omega_n$. Moreover, analysis will show that phase of the response goes through zero degrees at $\omega = \omega_n$. Thus for the special case of high gain it is very easy to determine ω_n.

Damping is a little cumbersome to obtain, but it, too, can be obtained, although by indirect means. The magnitude of response of (9-9b) at $\omega = \omega_n$ is

$$\left| \frac{V_d(j\omega_n)}{V_x(j\omega_n)} \right| = \left| \frac{K_o K_d}{j\omega_n + K_o K_d\, F(j\omega_n)} \right| \qquad (9\text{-}10)$$

By using (2-10) and Figure 2-2, the magnitude can variously be found to be

$$\left| \frac{V_d(j\omega_n)}{V_x(j\omega_n)} \right| = \frac{K_o K_d}{\omega_n{}^2 \tau_2} = \frac{K_o K_d}{2\zeta\omega_n} = \frac{\tau_1 \omega_n}{2\zeta}$$

* Response of a low-gain loop will be somewhat modified but not grossly different.

so that damping is calculated as

$$\zeta = \frac{\tau_1 \omega_n}{2} \left| \frac{V_d(j\omega_n)}{V_x(j\omega_n)} \right|^{-1} \qquad (9\text{-}11)$$

$$\zeta = \frac{\omega_n \tau_2}{2} \qquad (9\text{-}12)$$

or

$$\zeta = \frac{K_o K_d}{2\omega_n} \left| \frac{V_d(j\omega_n)}{V_x(j\omega_n)} \right|^{-1} \qquad (9\text{-}13)$$

That is to say, if ω_n is determined and response magnitude at $\omega = \omega_n$ is measured, damping may be inferred if one of the three time constants (τ_1, τ_2, or $1/K_o K_d$) of the loop is known.

Transient Responses

Linear transient measurements can be performed by using any of the test arrangements shown for frequency responses. All that is required is that the test voltage V_x have the appropriate waveshape (step, ramp, and so forth) rather than the sine wave used for frequency response. Note that for transient inputs the output quantity of greatest interest is usually phase error. In those test arrangements in which error response is not shown (particularly Figure 9-4) some provision must be made to obtain the desired function.

Linearity of operation must be examined closely.* Obviously, if the modulating signal is large enough, the loop will be driven into its nonlinear range, thereby violating all of the assumptions used in deriving loop transfer functions. Ensuing response may be very different from the linear response being sought.

Of course, the purpose of the testing may very well be to determine non-linear response of the loop, in which case, it is necessary to ensure that the correct nonlinearity is being exercised. If the test setup exactly duplicates the expected operational conditions, there will be no difficulty encountered. However, when a synthetic transfer function is measured by inserting a modulating voltage V_x directly into the loop (as in Figure 9-5), it is conceivable that the resulting nonlinear response will be completely unrealistic.

An example will illustrate one possible discrepancy. If a loop is tracking a signal with zero phase error, an input phase jump of any arbitrary

* Linearity in frequency-response measurement is also important. However, non-linearities appear as distortion of the sine wave and are likely to be recognized and corrected. In transient measurements the distortion is less likely to be recognized.

magnitude may be applied and the loop will remain in lock. There will be a transient phase error, but the loop will eventually return to perfect tracking.

An input phase step in Figure 9-3 is equivalent to a step change in V_x in Figure 9-5. If the magnitude of V_x is sufficiently large, the loop will jump out of lock and possibly stay out. If V_x is small enough for the loop to hold lock, V_2 will eventually return to zero (or whatever other value it had before the step), but a steady-state loop phase error of a magnitude that will cancel V_x exactly is now required.

The change of phase error moves the loop operating point to a different location on the phase-detector characteristic, so that loop gain and bandwidth at the end of the transient are changed from those just before the start. In the configuration of Figure 9-3 there is no steady-state error (due to a phase step), and therefore, the before and after gains and bandwidths are the same. There will, of course, be variation during the transient.

Because of the differing variations of gain and bandwidth, it is inevitable that the "error" quantities measured (V_d in Figure 9-3 and V_2 in Figure 9-5) for the two different techniques will be different. The transient shapes will approach identity as magnitude of the step decreases. That is to say, the linear responses—implying vanishingly small inputs—of the two techniques will be the same but the nonlinear responses must differ.

9-4   Noise Measurements

Threshold

From an equipment standpoint determination of the unlock threshold of a phaselocked receiver is a simple matter. All that is required is a stable signal generator with a calibrated low-level output and some means of distinguishing between lock and unlock. The receiver is first synchronized with a strong signal, and then the level is reduced until the lock is lost. Signal level at unlock is recorded as the receiver's threshold.

Surely this is a simple enough procedure, but unhappily repetition of the test will yield a different number for threshold level. Such uncertainty should be expected from the earlier discussion in Chapter 3. Loss of lock is a random statistical phenomenon and not deterministic. Some variations in consecutive measurements are therefore unavoidable.

A variation of several decibels over a series of many trials is likely, and some kind of "best" result must be determined from the scattered data. A theoretical value (based on receiver noise figure, loop bandwidth, and a reasonable theoretical definition of threshold) ought not to disagree with the measurement by more than a few decibels. Any greater discrepancy is an indication of a faulty receiver or unrealistic theoretical model.

Phase Jitter

Another quantity often sought is the output phase jitter caused by noise. In Chapter 3 the mean-square value of the jitter was denoted as $\overline{\theta_{no}{}^2}$. In order to measure output noise jitter it is necessary to compare a clean version of the input signal against the VCO output. The arrangement of Figure 9-2 is appropriate.

As already explained, a coherent frequency translator will be needed if the VCO is not at the same frequency as the signal. This necessity is a decided complication but cannot be avoided. In particular, noise jitter cannot be observed by measuring output from the loop phase detector. The noise appearing at the PD is virtually the entire amount of input noise present and is far in excess of the noise-induced jitter.

The most meaningful description of jitter is its rms value. (However, see Chapter 3 for a discussion of nonstationarity and the necessity to regard phase-error modulo 2π.) To this end, a "true rms" voltmeter connected to the output of the precision (calibrated) phase detector of Figure 9-2 would provide a measure of the rms phase jitter.

Care must be exercised in the choice of instruments and interpretation of data in this measurement. Most electronic "true rms" meters are capacitance-coupled at their input and their cutoff frequency is in the neighborhood of 5 to 20 Hz. If, as is likely, loop bandwidth is comparable to or less than the meter cutoff frequency, most of the jitter power will be rejected by the meter and the reading will be erroneous.

Ideally, a suitable meter should have response extending down to direct current (a thermocouple, an electrodynamometer, or a calorimetric wattmeter) in order to accept all of the jitter power. With such a meter, the average phase error must be adjusted carefully to zero; the meter is unable to distinguish between jitter and d-c offset.

Also, the meter will follow the slowest jitter fluctuations and thereby tend to give a reading of instantaneous rather than average jitter power. A large time constant in the meter is needed to counteract this tendency. To this end a calorimetric wattmeter, with its inherently slow response, may prove useful.

In another approach an oscillographic recording is made of the jitter and an estimate of mean-square value is actually computed by taking many samples. An ultimate extension of this tedious process would be to sample automatically, digitize the sample values, and allow a computer to calculate mean-square values. Such a process does not currently seem feasible as a laboratory technique, but the computer art is advancing rapidly, and who knows what the future may bring into the lab?

More commonly, the oscillograph record will be "filtered" visually, and the rms estimated approximately from some rule of thumb. (One such rule that is prevalent, although hardly rigorous, states that the rms is one third of the "average" peak of the noise waveform. With a little practice, estimates accurate to 20 percent can be achieved.)

Jitter is not caused exclusively by noise—some is inherent to the loop oscillator(s), primarily the VCO. Inherent jitter is measured with an essentially noise-free input signal to prevent noise-masking. Measurements can be made at the loop phase detector (assuming proper calibration), and no external phase detector is needed. (See Chapter 5 for an analysis of VCO jitter.) Otherwise, the measurement problems are similar to those encountered in the measurement of noise jitter.

Noise Bandwidth

Noise bandwidth is another loop parameter of great interest. Direct measurement is not easy, but an indirect determination can be made by using the measured amplitude frequency response $H(f)$ and the relation

$$B_L = \int_0^\infty |H(f)|^2 \, df \qquad (9\text{-}14)$$

The integration can be performed numerically or graphically and a useful answer obtained.

In a high-gain, second-order loop the noise bandwidth is related to natural frequency and damping by (4-12). The quantities ω_n and ζ can be obtained by simple measurements, as explained in Section 9-3, and B_L is calculated therefrom.

Another approach is to recognize that synthetic transfer functions, measured by inserting a test modulating voltage V_x (see Section 9-3) into the loop, have the same noise bandwidth as the actual loop transfer function. If white noise of known spectral density N_x volts²/Hz is inserted into the loop in place of V_x (see Figure 9-5), there will be a mean-square noise response of $\overline{v_F^2(t)}$. Noise bandwidth must therefore be

$$B_L = \frac{\overline{v_F^2(t)}}{N_x} \text{ Hz} \qquad (9\text{-}15)$$

As far as is known, this approach has never been tried. In addition to precautions to be taken regarding loop nonlinearities (see the discussion under "Transient Response" in the preceding section), the noise test equipment is not likely to have suitable characteristics at low frequencies.

The problems with rms voltmeters have already been mentioned; similarly, available noise generators are not flat much below 20 Hz and have zero output at direct current.

Therefore with existing commercial equipment a synthetic noise measurement is not overly feasible. Nonetheless, if special equipment were built or loop bandwidth were wide enough to allow the use of commercial instruments, the technique would hold the promise of substantial convenience and simplicity.

Bandwidth Variations

We have shown elsewhere (Chapter 5) that noise will cause signal suppression if a limiter or wideband AGC is used. As a consequence, loop gain, and therefore bandwidth and loop dynamics, will vary with input SNR. Any gain-related loop parameters must be measured at specified SNR's or at least at specified signal levels. The parameters will change as signal level changes.

Sometimes it is necessary to measure parameter variation as a function of signal-to-noise ratio. If the parameter depends on noise (e.g., noise jitter) or the measurement can tolerate the presence of noise (possibly measurements of d-c phase error), it is necessary merely to vary the input SNR in any convenient manner.

Measurements of some other parameters are badly obscured by the presence of noise, in which case a noise-free signal is required and loop gain may be adjusted by inserting an attenuator between the phase-detector input and limiter output. Signal suppression is thereby simulated without introduction of noise.

References

And-1   T. C. Anderson and F. G. Merrill, "Crystal-Controlled Primary Frequency Standards: Latest Advances for Long-Term Stability," *Trans IRE*, **I-9**, pp. 136–140, September 1960.

Att-1   W. R. Attkinson, L. Fey and J. Newman, "Spectrum Analysis of Extremely Low Frequency Variations of Quartz Oscillators," *Proc. IRE*, Vol. 51, p. 379, February 1963.

Bal-1   M. Balodis, "Laboratory Comparison of Tan-Lock and Phase-Lock," *National Telemetering Conference*, Paper 5–4, 1964.

Bar-1   R. D. Barnard, "Variational Techniques Applied to Capture in Phase-Controlled Oscillators," *BSTJ*, Vol. 41, pp. 227–256, January 1962.

Bel-1   H. de Bellescize, "La Reception Synchrone," *Onde Elect.*, Vol. 11, pp. 230–240, June 1932.

Ben-1   A. Benjaminson, "Phase-Locked Klystrons Simulate Doppler Radar," *Electronics*, pp. 44–46, April 19, 1963.

Ben-2   A. Benjaminson, "Phase-Locking Microwave Oscillators to Improve Stability and Frequency Modulation," *Microwave Journal*, pp. 88–92, January 1963.

Ben-3   A. Benjaminson, "Phase-Locked Microwave Oscillator Systems with 0.1 cps Stability," *Microwave Journal*, pp. 65–69, December 1964.

Bic-1   R. W. Bickmore, "Adaptive Antenna Arrays," *Spectrum*, Vol. I, pp. 78–88, August 1964.

Bre-1   M. Breese, R. Colbert, W. Rubin, and P. Sferrazza, "Phase-Locked Loops for Electronically Scanned Antenna Arrays," *Trans IRE*, **SET-7**, pp. 95–100, December 1961.

Bro-1   M. H. Brockman, H. R. Buchanan, R. L. Choate, and L. Malling, "Extra-terrestrial Radio Tracking and Communications," *Proc. IRE*, Vol. 48, pp. 643–655, April 1960.

Bur-1   E. E. Burnett, "A K_u-Band Phase-Locked System," *Proc. 1963 Nat. Winter Conv. on Military Electronics*.

Byr-1   C. J. Byrne, "Properties and Design of the Phase-Controlled Oscillator with a Sawtooth Comparator," *BSTJ*, pp. 559–602, March 1962.

Cla-1   J. K. Clapp and F. D. Lewis, "A Unique Standard-Frequency Multiplier," *IRE Nat. Conv. Rec.*, Part 5, 1957.

Cos-1   J. P. Costas, "Synchronous Communications," *Proc. IRE*, Vol. 44, pp. 1713–1718, December 1956.

Dav-1   W. B. Davenport, Jr., "Signal-to-Noise Ratios in Band-Pass Limiters," *J. Appl. Phys.*, **24**, pp. 720–727, June 1953.

Deb-1   L. G. de Bey, "Tracking in Space by DOPLOC," *Trans. IRE*, **MIL-4**, pp. 332–335, April–July 1960.

Dev-1   J. A. Develet, Jr., "A Threshold Criterion for Phase-Lock Demodulator," *Proc. IEEE*, Vol. 51, pp. 349–356, February 1963.

Dev-2   J. A. Develet,"An Analytic Approximation of Phase-Lock Receiver Threshold," *Trans. IEEE*, **SET-9**, pp. 9–11, March 1963.

Dev-3   J. A. Develet, Jr., "The Influence of Time Delay on Second-Order Phase Lock Loop Acquisition Range," *Internat. Telem. Conf.*, pp. 432–437, London, 1963.

Dis-1   R. H. Dishington, "Diode Phase Discriminators," *Proc. IRE*, Vol. 37, pp. 1401–1404, December 1949.

Eds-1   W. A. Edson, "Noise in Oscillators," *Proc. IRE*, Vol. 48, pp. 1454–1467, August 1960.

Enl-1   L. H. Enloe and J. L. Rodda, "Laser Phase-Locked Loop," *Proc. IEEE*, Vol. 53, p. 165, February 1965.

Esp-1   R. Esposito and J. A. Mullen, "Noise in Oscillators with General Tank Circuits," *IRE Conv. Rec.*, Part 4, pp. 202–208, 1961.

Fel-1   E. P. Felch and J. O. Israel, "A Simple Circuit for Frequency Standards Employing Overtone Crystals," *Proc. IRE*, Vol. 43, pp. 596–603, May 1955.

Fey-1   L. Fey, W. R. Atkinson, J. Newman, and L. Malling, "Obscurities of Oscillator Noise," *Proc. IEEE*, Vol. 52, pp. 104–106, January 1964.

Fra-1   J. P. Frazier and J. Page, "Phase-Lock Loop Frequency Acquisition Study," *Trans. IRE*, **SET-8**, pp. 210–227, September 1962.

Gar-1   F. M. Gardner, "DOPLOC Uses Phase-Locked Filter," *Electronic Industries*, Vol. 18, pp. 96–99, October 1959.

Gar-3   F. M. Gardner, "An Improved DOVAP Transponder," 1960 *IRE Wescon Record*, Part V, pp. 174–181.

Gil -1   C. E. Gilchriest, "Application of the Phase-Locked Loop to Telemetry as a Discriminator or Tracking Filter," *Trans. IRE*, **TRC-4**, pp. 20–35, June 1958.

Gol-2   A. J. Goldstein, "Analysis of the Phase-Controlled Loop with a Sawtooth Comparator," *BSTJ*, Vol. 41, pp. 603–633, March 1962.

Gol-3   A. J. Goldstein and C. J. Byrne, "Pull-In Frequency of the Phase-Controlled Oscillator," *Proc. IRE*, Vol. 49, p. 1209, July 1961.

Gol-4   R. Goldstein, "The Minimization of Oscillator Noise," *JPL Research Summary No.* 36–14, pp. 61–63, May 1, 1962.

Gol-5   M. J. E. Golay, "Monochromaticity and Noise in a Regenerative Electric Oscillator," *Proc. IRE*, Vol. 48, pp. 1472–1477, August 1960.

Gri-1   P. Grivet and A. Blaquiere, "Non-Linear Effects of Noise in Electronic Clocks," *Proc. IEEE*, Vol. 51, pp. 1606–1614, November 1963.

Gru-1   W. J. Gruen, "Theory of AFC Synchronization," *Proc. IRE*, Vol. 41, pp. 1043–1048, August 1953.

Gup-1   S. C. Gupta, "Transient Analysis of a Phase-Locked Loop Optimized for a Frequency Ramp Input," *Trans. IEEE*, **SET-10**, pp. 79–83, June 1964.

Hig-1   W. H. Highleyman and E. S. Jacob, "An Analog Multiplier Using Two Field Effect Transistors," *Trans. IRE*, **CS-10**, pp. 311–317, September 1962.

Hof-1   L. A. Hoffman, *Receiver Design and the Phase-Lock Loop*, Aerospace Corporation, El Segundo, May 1963, (Booklet prepared for Electronics and Space Exploration Lecture Series. Sponsored by Los Angeles IEEE).

Jaf-1   R. Jaffe and E. Rechtin, "Design and Performance of Phase-Lock Loops Capable of Near-Optimum Performance Over a Wide Range of Input Signal and Noise Levels," *Trans. IRE*, **IT-1**, pp. 66–76, March 1955.

Joh-1   Walter A. Johnson, "A General Analysis of the False-Lock Problem Associated with the Phase-Lock Loop," Report TDR-269 (4250–45)-1, Aerospace Corporation, October 2, 1963. (NASA Accession N64-13776.)

Jpl-6   "VCO Stability," *JPL Research Summary No. 36–3*, pp. 52–53.

Jpl-7   "RF Voltage-Controlled Oscillator Developments," *JPL Space Programs Summary No. 37–15*, Vol. III, pp. 34–36, May 31, 1962.

Lin-1   W. C. Lindsey, "Optimum Frequency Demodulation," *JPL Space Programs Summary No. 37–26*, Vol. IV, pp. 227–234, April 30, 1964.

Lin-3   W. C. Lindsey, "Threshold Characteristics in Phase-Locked Frequency Discriminators," *JPL Space Programs Summary No. 37–28*, Vol. IV, pp. 223–226, August 31, 1964.

Lin-4   W. C. Lindsey, "Investigation of Second-Order Phase-Locked Loops by Fokker-Planck Methods," *JPL Space Programs Summary, No. 37–30*, Vol. IV, pp. 262–268, December 31, 1964.

Mal-1   L. R. Malling, "Phase-Stable Oscillators for Space Communications, Including the Relationship Between the Phase Noise, the Spectrum, the Short-Term Stability, and the Q of the Oscillator," *Proc. IRE*, Vol. 50, pp. 1656–1664, July 1962.

Mar-3   B. D. Martin, "The Pioneer IV Lunar Probe: A Minimum-Power FM/FM System Design," Technical Report No. 32-215, *JPL*, March 1962.

Mar-6   T. B. Martin, "Circuit Applications of the Field-Effect Transistor," *Semicon. Prod.*, Vol. 5, Part I, pp. 33–39, February 1962, Part II, pp. 30–38, March 1962.

Mul-1   J. A. Mullen, "Background Noise in Oscillators," *Proc. IRE*, Vol. 48, pp. 1467–1473, August 1960.

Nis-1   T. Nishimura, "Design of Phase-Locked Loop Systems with Correlated Noise Input," *JPL Space Programs Summary No. 37–26*, Vol. IV, pp. 234–240, April 30, 1964.

Ped-1   B. O. Pedersen, "Phase-Sensitive Detection with Multiple Frequencies," *Trans. IRE*, **I-9**, pp. 349–354, December 1960.

Pet-1   M. Peter and M. W. P. Strandberg, "Phase Stabilization of Microwave Oscillators," *Proc. IRE*, Vol. 43, pp. 869–873, July 1955.

Pie-1   John A. Pierce, "Intercontinental Frequency Comparison by VLF Radio Transmission," *Proc. IRE*, Vol. 45, pp. 794–803, June 1957.

Poy-1   R. L. Poynter and G. R. Steffensen, "Tunable High Stability Microwave Oscillator," *Rev. Sci. Inst.*, Vol. 34, pp. 77–82, January 1963.

Rec-1   E. Rechtin, "The Design of Optimum Linear Systems," *JPL External Pub. No. 204*, April 1953.

Rey-1   T. J. Rey, "Automatic Phase Control: Theory & Design," *Proc. IRE*, Vol. 48, pp. 1760–1771, October 1960; corrections in *Proc. IRE*, p. 590, March, 1961.

Rey-2   T. J. Rey, "Further on the Phase-Locked Loop in the Presence of Noise," *Proc. IEEE*, Vol. 53, p. 494–495, May 1965.

Ric-1   D. Richman, "APC Color Sync for NTSC Color Television," *IRE Conv. Rec.*, Part 4, 1953.

Ric-2   D. Richman, "Color-Carrier Reference Phase Synchronization Accuracy in NTSC Color Television," *Proc. IRE*, Vol. 42, pp. 106–133, January 1954.

Ric-3   D. Richman, "DC Quadricorrelator: A Two Mode Sync System," *Proc. IRE*, Vol. 42, pp. 288–299, January 1954.

Rob-2   L. M. Robinson, "TANLOCK: A Phase-Lock Loop of Extended Tracking Capability," *Proc. 1962 Conv. on Military Electronics*, February 7–9, Los Angeles.

Rue-1   A. K. Rue and P. A. Lux, "Transient Analysis of a Phase-Lock Loop Discriminator," *Trans. IRE*, **SET-7**, pp. 105–111, December 1961.

Run-1   R. A. Runyan, "Factors Affecting Choice of Loop Filters in Phase-Locked Loop Discriminators," *Proc. 1959 Nat. Symp. on Space Electronics and Telem.*, Paper 9–1.

San-1   R. W. Sanneman and J. R. Rowbotham, "Unlock Characteristics of the Optimum Type II Phase-Locked Loop," *Trans. IEEE*, **ANE-11**, pp. 15–24, March 1964.

San-2   K. H. Sann, "Phase Stability of Oscillators," *Proc. IRE*, Vol. 49, pp. 527–528, February 1961.

Seh-6   K. Schlesinger, "Lock Oscillator for Television Synchronization," *Electronics* Vol. 22, pp. 112–117, January 1949.

Smi-1   W. L. Smith, "Miniature Transistorized Crystal-Controlled Precision Oscillators," *Trans. IRE*, **I-9**, pp. 141–148, September 1960.

Spi-3   J. J. Spilker, Jr., "Threshold Comparison of Phase-Lock, Frequency-Lock and Maximum Likelihood Types of FM Discriminators," Paper 14/2 presented at WESCON, San Francisco, 1961.

Sti-1   J. J. Stiffler, "The Squaring Loop Technique for Binary PSK Synchronization," *JPL Space Programs Summary No. 37–26*, Vol. IV, pp. 240–246, Pasadena, April, 30 1964.

Str-1   R. G. Strauch, "Phase Locking Millimeter Sources for Frequency Control," *Frequency*, Prototype Issue, pp. 16–18, 1962.

Str-2   M. W. P. Strandberg, "Noise Spectrum of Phase-Locked Oscillators," *Proc. IRE*, Vol. 48, pp. 1168–1169, June 1960.

Str-3   H. P. Stratemeyer, "A Low-Noise Phase Locked Oscillator Multiplier," *Interim Proc. Symp. on Definition & Measurement of Short-Term Frequency Stability*, Part III, pp. 121–136, Goddard Space Flight Center, Greenbelt Md., December 1964.

Syk-1   R. A. Sykes, W. L. Smith and W. J. Spencer, "Performance of Precision Quartz-Crystal Frequency Generators," *Trans. IRE*, **I-11**, pp. 243–247, December 1962.

Tau-1   R. C. Tausworthe, "New Calculation of Phase-Locked Loop Performance," *JPL Space Programs Summary No. 37–31*, Vol. IV, pp. 292–300, February 1965.

Tik-1   V. I. Tikhonov, "Phase-Lock Automatic Frequency Control Application in the Presence of Noise," *Automatika: Telemekanika* 23, 3, 1960.

Tik-2   V. I. Tikhonov, "The Effect of Noise on Phase-Lock Oscillation Operation," *Automatica: Telemekanika* 22, 9, 1959.

Van-2   Harry L. VanTrees, "Functional Techniques for the Analysis of the Non-Linear Behavior of Phase-Locked Loops," *Proc. IEEE*, Vol. 52, pp. 894–911, August 1964.

Vic-1   W. K. Victor, "The Evaluation of Phase-Stable Oscillators for Coherent Communication Systems," *JPL External Publication No. 337*, May 8, 1956.

Vic-2   W. K. Victor and M. H. Brockman, "The Application of Linear Servo Theory to the Design of AGC Loops," *JPL External Publication No. 586*, December 22, 1958; *Proc. IRE*, Vol. 48, pp. 234–238, February 1960.

Vit-1   A. J. Viterbi, "Acquisition and Tracking Behavior of Phase-Locked Loops," *JPL External Publication No. 673*, July 14, 1959.

Vit-2   A. J. Viterbi, "Phase-Locked Loop Dynamics in the Presence of Noise by Fokker-Planck Techniques," *Proc. 7th Regional IEEE Conv.*, April 1963; Technical Report No. 32–427, *JPL*, March 29, 1963.

Vit-5   A. J. Viterbi, "Phase-Locked Loop Dynamics in the Presence of Noise by Fokker-Planck Techniques," *Proc. IEEE*, Vol. 51, pp. 1737–1753, December 1963.

War-1   A. W. Warner, "Design and Performance of an Ultra Precise 2.5 mc Quartz-Crystal Unit," *BSTJ*, Vol. 34, pp. 1193–1217, September 1960.

Wen-1   K. R. Wendt and G. L. Fredendall, "Automatic Frequency and Phase Control of Synchronization in Television Receivers," *Proc. IRE*, Vol. 31, pp. 7–15, January 1943.

Appendix A

Mathematical review

This appendix is a collection of some of the underlying mathematics used in analysis of phaselock loops. Since it is intended solely as a brief review and not as a rigorous development, the pertinent results are stated without proof. References are provided for the reader who wants greater detail.

A-1 Network Analysis

Laplace Transforms

It is convenient to make use of the concepts and notation of Laplace transforms. (The standard engineering reference on the subject is M. F. Gardner and J. L. Barnes, *Transients in Linear Systems*, Wiley, New York, 1942.) We denote the Laplace complex variable (sometimes called "complex frequency") by the symbol $s = \sigma + j\omega$.

For any physical time function $x(t)$, such that $x(t) = 0$ if $t < 0$, there is a function $X(s)$ which is the Laplace transform of $x(t)$. Similarly, for every suitable complex function $X(s)$ there is a unique time function $x(t)$ which is the inverse Laplace transform of $X(s)$. These relations may be symbolized by the transform pairs

$$L[x(t)] = X(s)$$
$$L^{-1}[X(s)] = x(t)$$

Several transform pairs used in this book are tabulated at the top of the next page.

Transfer Functions

Consider a linear, constant-element, two-port, electrical network to which is applied an input signal $x_{in}(t)$ and which in response delivers an output signal $x_o(t)$. The Laplace transforms of the signals are $X_{in}(s)$ and $X_o(s)$, respectively.

	$x(t)$	$X(s)$
Unit step	1	$\dfrac{1}{s}$
Unit ramp	t	$\dfrac{1}{s^2}$
Exponential	e^{-at}	$\dfrac{1}{s+a}$
Derivative	$\dfrac{dy(t)}{dt}$	$s\,Y(s) - y(0+)$
Definite integral	$\displaystyle\int_0^t y(t)\,dt$	$\dfrac{1}{s}\,Y(s)$
Final value	$\displaystyle\lim_{t\to\infty} x(t)$	$\displaystyle\lim_{s\to 0} s\,Y(s)$

The transfer function of the network is defined as

$$F(s) = \frac{X_o(s)}{X_{in}(s)}$$

For all purposes of this book, $F(s)$ will be the ratio of two polynomials in s.

$$F(s) = \frac{a_m s^m + a_{m-1} s^{m-1} + \cdots a_o}{b_n s^n + b_{n-1} s^{n-1} + \cdots b_o}$$

$$x_i(t) \longrightarrow \boxed{\text{Network}} \longrightarrow x_o(t)$$

Figure A-1   Two-port network.

($m \leq n$ for a realizable network.) A polynomial may be factored and expressed as a product of its roots.

$$F(s) = \frac{a_m(s - z_m)(s - z_{m-1}) \cdots (s - z_1)}{b_n(s - p_n)(s - p_{n-1}) \cdots (s - p_1)}$$

Roots of the numerator are called zeros, whereas roots of the denominator are called poles. There are m zeros and n poles. Roots may be plotted in the complex s-plane as illustrated in Figure A-2. Complex roots must appear in conjugate pairs, whereas real roots may appear alone. Poles must appear in only the left half-plane (LHP) if the network is to be stable (realizable). Zeros may appear anywhere, but we are concerned only with networks whose zeros are in the LHP (minimum phase networks).

Frequency Response

The frequency response of a network—that is, the steady-state response to a sinusoidal input—is directly related to the transfer function as now described. Suppose the input to a network is of the form

$$x_{in}(t) = \sin \omega t$$

Then the steady-state output will be

$$x_o(t) = A(\omega) \sin [\omega t + \phi(\omega)]$$

where $A(\omega)$ is the amplitude of the output and $\phi(\omega)$ is the phase. A graph of A and ϕ plotted versus ω shows the frequency response of the network.

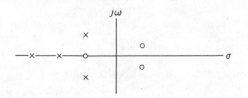

Figure A-2   Pole-zero diagram. $\bigcirc$ = zeros, $\times$ = poles.

The transfer function of the network may be written for the condition $s = j\omega$ (i.e., $\sigma = 0$). Wherever s appears in the expression $F(s)$, we substitute $j\omega$ instead, thereby obtaining $F(j\omega)$. Written in polar form,

$$F(j\omega) = |F(j\omega)| \exp \text{Arg} \, F(j\omega)$$

$$= A(\omega)e^{j\phi(\omega)}$$

That is, the magnitude of the transfer function for $s = j\omega$ is equal to the amplitude of the frequency response of the network, and the argument (phase) of the transfer function is equal to the phase of the frequency response.

EXAMPLES. Several common networks are often encountered in phase-lock circuits; their transfer functions and some properties of interest are presented here.

First consider a generalized inverted-L network consisting of series and shunt impedance arms, as in Figure A-3. The transfer function is

$$F(s) = \frac{E_o(s)}{E_{in}(s)} = \frac{Z_2(s)}{Z_1(s) + Z_2(s)}$$

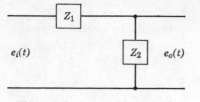
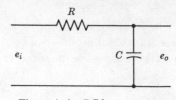

Figure A-3   Inverted-L network.   Figure A-4 RC lag network.

One particular L-network (Figure A-4) uses a resistor in the series arm and a capacitor as the shunt arm. Therefore, $Z_1 = R$, $Z_2 = 1/sC$, and the transfer function is

$$F(s) = \frac{1/sC}{R + 1/sC}$$

$$= \frac{1}{sCR + 1}$$

Frequency response, obtained by substituting $s = j\omega$, is

$$F(j\omega) = \frac{1}{j\omega CR + 1}$$

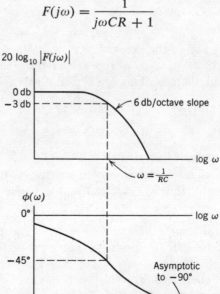

Figure A-5   Frequency response of lag network.

Magnitude of the frequency response is

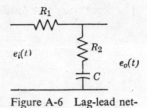

$$|F(j\omega)| = [F(j\omega)\,F(-j\omega)]^{\frac{1}{2}}$$
$$= (1 + \omega^2 R^2 C^2)^{-\frac{1}{2}}$$

and the phase is

$$\phi(\omega) = -\tan^{-1}\omega CR$$

Figure A-6 Lag-lead network.

It is often convenient to plot frequency response on a logarithmic frequency abscissa and also to plot magnitude on a logarithmic (decibel) ordinate. Phase is almost invariably plotted on a linear ordinate. Some properties of these graphs are illustrated in Figure A-5.

Another network, widely used as the loop filter in many phaselock loops, is the lag-lead network shown in Figure A-6. In this case $Z_1 = R_1$, $Z_2 = R_2 + 1/sC$ and

$$F(s) = \frac{R_2 + 1/sC}{R_1 + R_2 + 1/sC}$$

$$= \frac{sCR_2 + 1}{sC(R_1 + R_2) + 1}$$

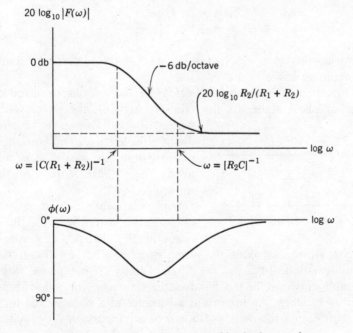

Figure A-7 Frequency response of lag-lead network.

The frequency response is

$$F(j\omega) = \frac{1 + j\omega R_2 C}{1 + j\omega C(R_1 + R_2)}$$

$$|F(j\omega)| = \left\{\frac{(1 + j\omega R_2 C)(1 - j\omega R_2 C)}{[1 + j\omega C(R_1 + R_2)][1 - j\omega C(R_1 + R_2)]}\right\}^{\frac{1}{2}}$$

$$= \left[\frac{1 + \omega^2 R_2^2 C^2}{1 + \omega^2 C^2 (R_1 + R_2)^2}\right]^{\frac{1}{2}}$$

$$\phi(j\omega) = \tan^{-1}\omega R_2 C - \tan^{-1}\omega C(R_1 + R_2)$$

and is sketched in Figure A-7.

Another network of practical significance is the simple bandpass tuned circuit of Figure A-8. The transfer function is

$$F(s) = \frac{sL/R}{s^2 LC + (sL/R) + 1}$$

from which the frequency response may be found to be

$$|F(j\omega)| = \frac{\omega L/R}{[(1 - \omega^2 LC)^2 + \omega^2 L^2/R^2]^{\frac{1}{2}}}$$

$$\phi(\omega) = \frac{\pi}{2} - \tan^{-1}\left(\frac{\omega L/R}{1 - \omega^2 LC}\right)$$

Frequency response is plotted in Figure A-9. (Note the linear frequency and magnitude scales.)

The tuned circuit example has been presented in order to introduce the concept of phase slope. In any selective network the phase shift ϕ is necessarily variable as a function of the frequency ω. The variation of phase within the passband is referred to as the "phase slope" of the response.

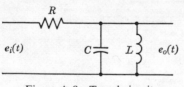

Figure A-8   Tuned circuit.

If information is carried in the phase of a signal and frequency of the signal is continually changing (e.g., the Doppler signal from a satellite), the phase slope will act to distort the desired information. In a passive filter, selectivity and phase slope are inextricably entwined; if the bandwidth is narrow, the phase slope will necessarily be steep. An important advantage of a phaselocked loop lies in the fact that narrow bandwidth can be attained with very small phase slope.

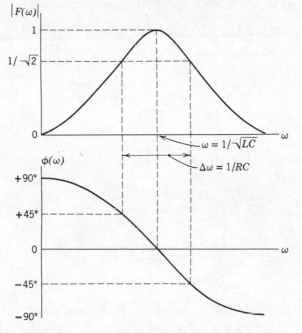

Figure A-9   Frequency response of tuned circuit.

A-2   Feedback

A phaselock loop is a feedback network, and a brief discussion of some aspects of feedback theory is presented here. For greater detail refer to any of the numerous books on control systems and servomechanisms (e.g., John G. Truxal, *Control System Synthesis*, McGraw-Hill, New York, 1955).

Basic Equations

A simple feedback loop is shown in Figure A-10. It consists of a forward-gain network with transfer function $A(s)$, a feedback network with transfer function $B(s)$, and a subtractor network that forms the difference between the input signal $y_i(t)$ and the output of the feedback network $y_f(t)$.

Writing the applicable equations in the transform domain yields

$$Y_d(s) = Y_{in}(s) - Y_f(s)$$

$$Y_o(s) = A(s)\, Y_d(s)$$

$$Y_f(s) = B(s)\, Y_o(s)$$

The signals y_i, y_d, and y_o are known as the input, error, and output signals, respectively.

Combining the three equations for the individual components, we obtain the closed-loop transfer function

$$H(s) = \frac{Y_o(s)}{Y_i(s)} = \frac{A(s)}{1 + A(s)\,B(s)}$$

and the closed-loop error response

$$\frac{Y_d(s)}{Y_i(s)} = \frac{1}{1 + A(s)\,B(s)}$$

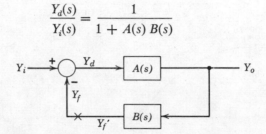

Figure A-10   Feedback loop.

To determine open-loop gain, break the loop at any point, say "x," and set $y_i = 0$. Apply a test signal y_f at the input side of the break and compute the resulting signal y_f' at the output side of the break. Open-loop gain is defined as

$$\frac{Y_f'(s)}{Y_f(s)} = -A(s)\,B(s)$$

In many cases (including phaselock loops) the transfer function of the feedback network $B = 1$. For that situation the closed-loop transfer function becomes

$$H(s) = \frac{A(s)}{1 + A(s)}$$

the error response is

$$\frac{Y_d(s)}{Y_i(s)} = \frac{1}{1 + A(s)} = 1 - H(s)$$

and the open-loop gain is simply $-A(s)$.

Stability

A feedback loop can oscillate if its open-loop gain exceeds unity and simultaneously its open-loop phase shift exceeds 180 degrees. At least one of the closed-loop poles of an unstable loop will lie in the right half of the s-plane. Analysis of stability by investigating pole location is done in Chapter 2 by the root-locus method. To apply this technique, the loop transfer function must be known in analytical form, and the locations of the open-loop poles and zeros must be known.

Stability can also be analyzed, without knowledge of the pole locations or even an analytical description of the transfer function, by means of Bode plots. (H. W. Bode, *Network Analysis and Feedback Amplifier Design*,

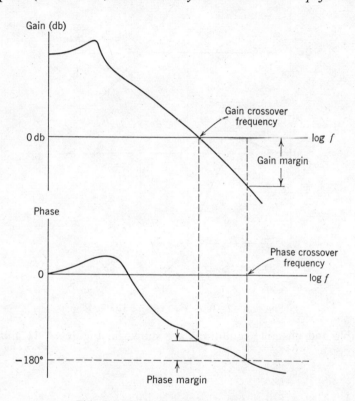

Figure A-11   Bode plot of a stable loop.

Van Nostrand, New York, 1945.) A Bode plot consists of the pair of graphs of the magnitude* and phase of the frequency response of open-loop gain, $A(s)\,B(s)$. Magnitude and frequency are both plotted on logarithmic scales.

The Bode criterion for unconditional† stability is that the gain must fall below unity (0 db) before the phase shift reaches 180 degrees. Illustrations

---

* Strictly speaking, in a *Bode* plot the magnitude is approximated by its asymptotes. We shall be free in our use of the terminology and let "Bode plot" include both the exact and approximate graphs of magnitude.

† A loop can be conditionally stable and still violate the Bode criterion.

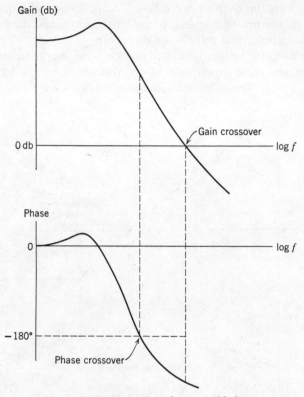

Figure A-12   Bode plot of an unstable loop.

of stable and unstable conditions are shown in Figures A-11 and A-12 respectively.

A-3   Noise Fundamentals

A major application of phaselock is to provide immunity against noise. This section briefly presents some of the more important concepts needed for the understanding of noise. Greater depth may be found in W. B. Davenport and W. L. Root, *Random Signals and Noise*, McGraw-Hill, New York, 1958.

We now consider a random noise voltage $n(t)$ and ask "How may it be described for analytical purposes?" For random noise the actual wave-shape is unpredictable, and it is not generally possible to write an explicit expression for $n(t)$. Any description must therefore be statistical in nature.

It is assumed that $n(t)$ is stationary; that is, all statistical properties are constant over all time. Most of the random quantities encountered in the study of phaselock may reasonably be considered stationary.

Statistical Properties

Important statistical properties of noise are listed in the following paragraphs.

1. Mean value (d-c value, average value).

$$\overline{n(t)} = \lim_{T \to \infty} \frac{1}{2T} \int_{-T}^{T} n(t)\, dt$$

The bar over a quantity denotes average value. We are usually concerned with noise voltages having zero mean.

2. Mean-square value (variance).

$$\overline{n^2(t)} = \lim_{T \to \infty} \frac{1}{2T} \int_{-T}^{T} n^2(t)\, dt$$

3. Probability density function is denoted as $p(n)$.

The integral $\int_{n_1}^{n_2} p(n)\, dn$ is the probability that the amplitude of a sample of $n(t)$ will lie in the range of n_1 to n_2. For any function to be a probability density, $p(n) \geq 0$ for all n and

$$\int_{-\infty}^{\infty} p(n)\, dn = 1$$

Previous averages (mean and mean-square) were time averages. Using probability density, we may express them as ensemble averages.

$$\overline{n} = \int_{-\infty}^{\infty} n\, p(n)\, dn$$

$$\overline{n^2} = \int_{-\infty}^{\infty} n^2\, p(n)\, dn$$

For ergodic stationary noise the ensemble and time averages are equal. (In the body of the book we have assumed ergodicity and not distinguished between time and ensemble averages.)

A very commonly encountered density is the *gaussian* or *normal* function. It is given by

$$p(n) = (2\pi\overline{n^2})^{-2} \exp \frac{-(n - \overline{n})^2}{2n^2}$$

4. Autocorrelation function.

$$R(\tau) = \lim_{T \to \infty} \frac{1}{2T} \int_{-T}^{T} n(t)\, n(t + \tau)\, dt$$

Autocorrelation is a very important quantity in its own right, but in this book it is used only to define the next statistical property.

5. Spectral density. This is defined as the Fourier transform of the autocorrelation function.

$$N(f) = \int_{-\infty}^{\infty} R(\tau)e^{-j\omega\tau}\, d\tau \qquad (\omega = 2\pi f)$$

It is also true that

$$R(\tau) = \int_{-\infty}^{\infty} N(f)e^{j\omega\tau}\, df$$

Spectral density is an extremely useful describer of the noise. It is an even function of frequency so that

$$N(f) = N(-f).$$

Spectral density integrated over all frequencies yields the variance

$$\int_{-\infty}^{\infty} N(f)\, df = \overline{n^2(t)}$$

A complete description of $N(f)$ may be obtained solely from its values at positive values of f. Thus, although mathematical definition of N results in a "two-sided density," it is also possible to speak of a "one-sided density" $N_1(f)$, which involves only positive frequencies; that is,

$$N_1(f) = 2N(f) \qquad (f \geq 0)$$
$$= 0 \qquad\qquad (f < 0)$$

As defined here, dimensions of N are in (volts)^2 per hertz, and N is therefore proportional to power. Density could be defined in a slightly different manner, and the dimensions would then be in watts per hertz. This second definition of power spectral density is denoted by the symbol $W(f)$ and in any particular case is related to $N(f)$ by a constant multiplier.

Despite the suggestive notation, it must not be thought that $N(f)$ is the Fourier transform of $n(t)$. For most noise functions the Fourier transform does not exist. If $n(t)$ were unusual and had a Fourier transform, $F[n(t)]$, then $F[n(t)] \neq N(f)$.

Noise is often passed through filters. If input spectral density is $N_i(f)$ and filter transfer function is $H(f)$, then the output spectrum is

$$N_o(f) = N_i(f)\, |H(f)|^2.$$

A convenient fiction often employed is the concept of "white noise." For this case $N(f)$ is constant for all frequencies. No physical process can be truly white, for that would imply infinite power. A practical definition of whiteness is that the noise spectral density is constant at all frequencies of interest. A white noise spectrum is completely specified by a single number: the spectral density at any frequency. It is necessary to state one-sided or two-sided spectrum.

Caution. Noise is very commonly specified as white gaussian noise. These are independent statements, and neither one implies the other. Noise can be nongaussian or nonwhite or both.

Noise Bandwidth

Suppose a noise voltage has a one-sided spectral density of $N(f)$ and that it is passed through a filter with transfer function of $H(j\omega)$. Variance of the output voltage of the filter is therefore

$$\overline{n_o^2} = \int_0^\infty N(f)|H(j\omega)|^2 \, df.$$

If the input spectrum is white, $N(f) = N$ is constant for all f, and the output variance becomes

$$\overline{n_o^2} = N\int_0^\infty |H(j\omega)|^2 \, df$$

At some reference frequency f_r, the transfer function has a magnitude of $H_r = |H(j\omega_r)|$.

There is an equivalent (though fictitious) rectangular filter, with constant magnitude of transmission equal to H_r and a bandwidth B_n (hertz), such that the variances of the outputs of the two filters are equal if they have white noise inputs of equal density; that is,

$$\overline{n_o^2} = NH_r^2B_n$$

for the rectangular filter.

Equating the two variances provides the definition of noise bandwidth as

$$B_n = |H(j\omega_r)|^{-2}\int_0^\infty |H(j\omega)|^2 \, df$$

Figure A-13 illustrates the relation between an actual low-pass filter and its fictitious rectangular characteristic which defines noise bandwidth.

It is usually convenient to take the reference frequency f_r to be direct current in the case of a low-pass filter and as the center frequency in the case of a bandpass filter. Often a definition can be found wherein f_r is taken as the frequency of maximum response of the filter. Such a definition can lead to anomalous results when there is bandedge peaking of the response (as in Figure A-13) and therefore is not used here.

A one-sided bandwidth has been defined in accordance with normal convention and engineering convenience. It would have been equally

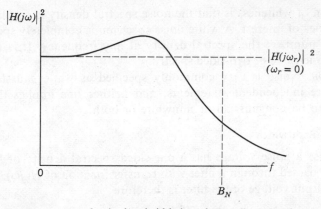

Figure A-13   Illustration of noise bandwidth (equal areas lie under the two curves).

feasible to define a two-sided noise bandwidth which would, of course, have turned out to be $2B_n$ for the same filter. The one-sided definition is used throughout this book.

Noise Temperature and Noise Figure

Consider an amplifier or receiver which has a (one-sided) bandwidth B and is connected to a signal source of some kind (such as an antenna). Noise is generated within the amplifier (receiver) and also within the source. *Noise temperature* of the entire system is defined by attributing all of the noise power generated to the source and considering the noise as thermal in origin, in which case the noise power referred to the source is given by

$$P_N = kT_eB$$

where k is Boltzmann's constant (1.38×10^{-23} joule/$^\circ K$), and T_e is the effective noise temperature of the system. The concept of noise temperature is most commonly applied in low-noise receiving systems.

Noise figure is a measure of the noisiness of the amplifier as compared with that of the source. Specifically, noise figure is defined as the ratio of the total noise power delivered by the amplifier to that portion of the noise that is due to the source alone. For a thermal noise source the system noise power, referred to the source, is

$$P_N = kT_sBF$$

where T_s is the noise temperature of the source and F is the noise figure. (Usually $10 \log_{10} F$—the noise figure in decibels—is the number specified.)

It is common practice to define a standard noise figure with reference to a standard thermal source at temperature $T_s = T_o = 290°$ K (i.e., slightly less than room temperature). For that condition $kT_o = 4 \times 10^{-21}$ watt/hertz. If the source is not at T_o, the actual operating noise figure is not equal to the standard noise figure; however, the error in noise power computed with the standard noise figure and $T_s = T_o$ will be small if the noise contribution of the receiver is much greater than that of the source.

At times it is useful to speak of the noise spectral density W rather than the total power. Spectral density is given by $W = P_N/B$. In terms of system noise temperature $W = kT_e$, whereas in terms of standard noise figure $W = FkT_o$.

Narrow-Band Noise

If a noise voltage $n(t)$ has associated with it a relatively narrow bandpass spectrum, it is permissible and often opportune to write

$$n(t) = n_c(t) \cos \omega_1 t - n_s(t) \sin \omega_1 t$$

where ω_1 is any arbitrary frequency whatever, but simplest results are usually obtained if it is selected as being in the center of the narrow passband.

Some properties of this expansion are as follows:

1. Spectrum. The spectra of n_c and n_s will be low-pass in nature.
2. Gaussian. If $n(t)$ is gaussian, n_c and n_s are also gaussian.
3. Mean. If $n(t)$ has zero mean, then n_c and n_s will also have zero mean value.
4. Variance.

$$\overline{n^2(t)} = \overline{n_c^2(t)} = \overline{n_s^2(t)}$$

5. Independence. The functions n_c and n_s are independent; that is

$$\overline{n_c(t)\, n_s(t)} = \overline{n_c(t)}\; \overline{n_s(t)}$$

$$= 0 \quad \text{if} \quad \overline{n(t)} = 0$$

6. Spectrum. Consider $n(t)$ to have a spectrum $W(f)$ defined as

$$W(f) = W_o \quad \text{if} \quad \left(f_1 - \frac{B}{2}\right) \leq f \leq \left(f_1 + \frac{B}{2}\right)$$

$$= 0 \quad \text{otherwise.}$$

That is, the spectrum of $n(t)$ is a bandpass rectangle of width B and height W_o centered at $f_1 = \omega_1/2\pi$.

For this case $n_c(t)$ and $n_s(t)$ will have spectra defined as

$$W_c(f) = W_s(f) = 2W_o \qquad f < \frac{B}{2}$$

$$= 0 \qquad\qquad\quad f > \frac{B}{2}$$

or, in other words, n_c and n_s have low-pass spectra of bandwidth $B/2$ and spectral density $2W_o$.

Appendix B

Design example

A numerical example illustrates the application of the material presented in the main body of the book. The example chosen is a portion of an actual preliminary design of an S-band transponder and is included here with the kind permission of Resdel Engineering Corporation of Pasadena, California.

The input frequency is specified as $2113\frac{5}{16}$ MHz, the output frequency as 2295 MHz for a coherent ratio of 240/221. A block diagram similar to that shown in Figure 8-3 is used with frequency multiplier ratios of $N_1 = 108$, $N_2 = 3$, $N_3 = \frac{1}{2}$, and $N_4 = 120$. Nominal frequencies are $47\frac{13}{16}$ MHz for the first IF, $9\frac{9}{16}$ MHz for the second IF, and $19\frac{1}{8}$ MHz for the VCO. If the diagram of Figure 8-3 is replaced with an equivalent (but fictitious) single conversion receiver as in Figure 7-1, the equivalent frequency multiplication of the VCO frequency will be $N = 110.5 = N_1 + N_2 - N_3$. (In actual practice, multipliers 1 and 2 are cascaded as a string composed of three triplers and two doublers with the injection for the second mixer tapped off from the output of the first tripler.)

Minimum signal power is specified as -135 dbm and represents the tracking threshold. Accordingly, threshold loop noise bandwidth will be chosen so that signal-to-noise ratio $(SNR)_L$ in the loop is 0 db for an input power of -135 dbm.

The received signal will have two subcarriers on it, one a sinewave at 70 kHz and the other a square wave at 500 kHz. Input power is divided between the phase modulation sidebands and a remaining carrier. Sinusoidal modulation affects carrier amplitude according to the zero-order Bessel function of the modulation index $J_o(\theta_m)$, whereas square-wave modulation affects the carrier as $\cos(\theta_m)$. Modulation indices are specified as 1.22 radians for the 70-kc sinusoidal subcarrier and 0.6 radian for the 500-kc pseudonoise, rectangular modulation. Amplitude of the surviving carrier is $J_o(1.22) \times \cos(0.6) = 0.66 \times 0.82 = 0.54$. This represents a reduction in carrier strength of nearly 5.5 db. Since the tracking loop is responsive to carrier only, the power available to the loop is 5.5 db below the total input power. At threshold the available power is therefore only −140.5 dbm.

The signal-to-noise ratio in the second IF amplifier is low, and therefore the limiter degrades the SNR by approximately 1 db. Therefore, to the tracking loop, the effective threshold power appears to be −141.5 dbm, which is 0.71×10^{-17} watts. This value of noise power in the loop is used to find the required threshold loop bandwidth.

Noise power is given by

$$P_n = FkT(2B_{LT})$$

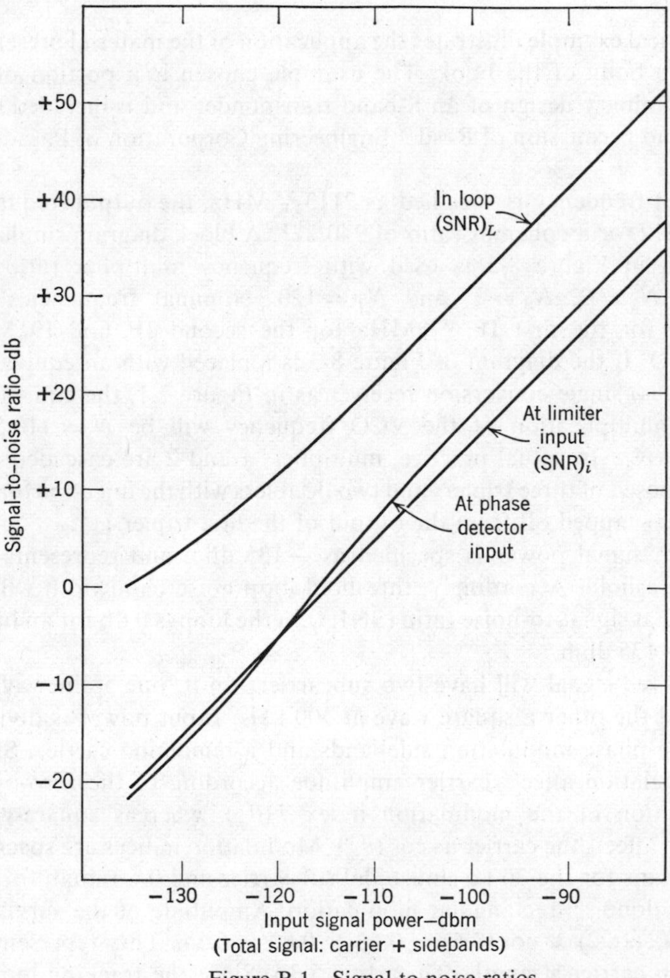

Figure B-1   Signal-to-noise ratios.

where we assume noise figure $F = +15.8$ (12 db) as a reasonable value. Also, $kT = 4 \times 10^{-21}$ watts/Hz, and B_{LT} is the loop bandwidth at threshold. Substituting the numbers shows $B_{LT} = 56$ Hz.

Bandwidth of the second IF filter is (tentatively) 10 kc at the 3-db points. The filter should consist of a single quartz crystal in order to avoid the large phase slope that accompanies more complex filters. In a single-tuned resonant circuit the noise bandwidth is $\pi/2$ times the 3-db bandwidth or 15.7 kc for the present case. Only the carrier will pass through this narrow filter; the modulation sidebands will be rejected.

Noise power in this bandwidth is $P_n = FkTB = 15.8 \times 4 \times 10^{-21} \times 15{,}700 = 10^{-15}$ watt, which is -120 dbm. At threshold, the IF SNR is therefore -20.5 db and the SNR into the phase detector (i.e., out of the limiter) is -21.5 db. The latter SNR is above the phase-detector threshold of approximately -30 db. (See Chapter 5.) Signal-to-noise ratios at limiter input and output are shown in Figure B-1 as a function of input signal power. The limiter preceding the phase detector suppresses the signal if it is smaller than the noise.

Suppression of the signal voltage is given by

$$\alpha = \left[\frac{(\text{SNR})_i}{4/\pi + (\text{SNR})_i} \right]^{\frac{1}{2}} \tag{5-4}$$

where $(\text{SNR})_i$ is the signal-to-noise ratio at the input to the limiter. The signal suppression factor α has been calculated and is shown as a function of input power in Figure B-2. At threshold $\alpha_T = 0.084$.

For a second-order loop the loop bandwidth is expressed as

$$B_L = B_{LT} \frac{[\alpha/\alpha_T + (4\zeta_T^2)^{-1}]}{[1 + (4\zeta_T^2)^{-1}]} \tag{5-5}$$

where ζ_T is loop damping factor at threshold. We have chosen $\zeta_T = 0.5$ in order to have the best Doppler-rate tracking capability. Loop bandwidth is plotted in Figure B-2. It may be seen that from 56 Hz at threshold bandwidth widens to 360 Hz at -90 dbm and stronger signals. If we know loop bandwidth and SNR into the phase detector, the loop signal-to-noise ratio $(\text{SNR})_L$ may be computed for various signal levels. The results are plotted in Figure B-1. Equation 3-14 is used to relate the two SNR's.

Damping factor ζ and loop natural frequency ω_n are also plotted in Figure B-2. In Chapter 5 it was shown that these are proportional to $\sqrt{\alpha}$. From ω_n and ζ it is then possible to determine the frequency response of

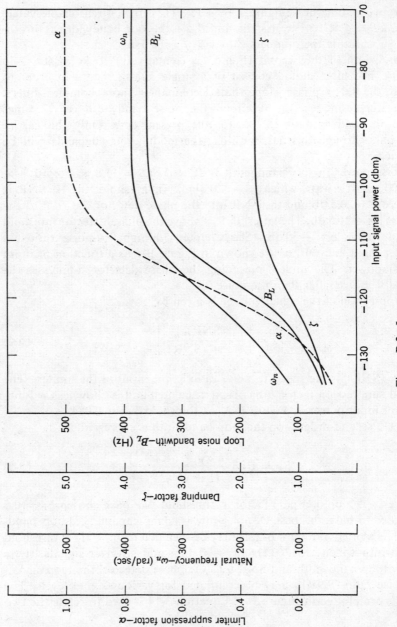

Figure B-2 Loop parameters.

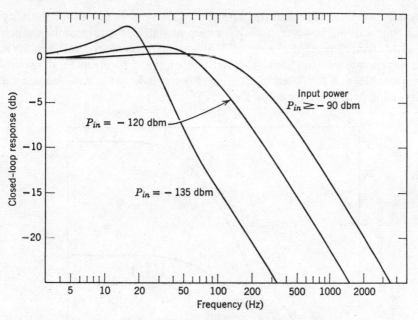

Figure B-3   Frequency response of tracking loop.

loop by utilizing Figure 2-3. Response is plotted in Figure B-3 for three representative signal levels.

Transponder phaselock is acquired by sweeping the frequency of the ground transmitter. Allowable sweep rate (and therefore acquisition time) is a function of the received signal level at the transponder. A theoretical upper limit exists on the permissible rate. If the sweep speed $\Delta \dot{f}$ exceeds $\omega_n^2/2\pi$, the loop can never lock up and, in fact, will lose lock if such a fast rate is applied after lock has been acquired. This upper limit is plotted in dashed lines in Figure B-4.

An empirical expression for sweep rate that takes account of noise disturbances is

$$\Delta \dot{f}_{90} = \frac{(1/2\pi)[1 - (\text{SNR})_L^{-\frac{1}{2}}](\alpha/\alpha_T)\omega_{nT}^2}{(1+d)} \tag{4-33}$$

where d is a factor related to the damping. This expression predicts the sweep rate that provides 90 percent probability of acquisition; it too is plotted in Figure B-4.

It may be seen that at high SNR, $\Delta \dot{f}_{90}$ asymptotically approaches the theoretical limit; to sweep so rapidly in a real situation is hazardous and is likely to lead to frequent missing of the signal. Some reduced rate is therefore necessary. If $\Delta \dot{f}_{90}$ actually provides a 90-percent probability of acquisition, two sweeps at this rate should afford a 99 percent probability of acquisition. However, a single sweep at half the rate promises much better than 99-percent chance of acquisition. Accordingly, at large SNR a sweep rate of $\frac{1}{2}(\omega_n^2/2\pi)$—that is, half of the theoretical limit—seems reasonable and has been plotted in Figure B-4. (This rate leads to a dynamic tracking error of 30 degrees.)

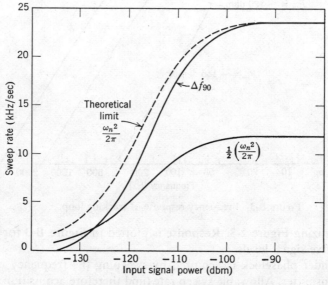

Figure B-4   Plot of search-rate equations.

Examination of the plot reveals that $\Delta \dot{f}_{90}$ and $\frac{1}{2}(\omega_n^2/2\pi)$ cross over at approximately -127 dbm. A conservative sweep rate would be determined by the smaller of the two plots. The total uncertainty of transponder frequency (including Doppler shift and VCO temperature drift) is 370 kHz, which is therefore the worst case of sweep range. If the frequency search is always over the full 370 kHz range, the average band searched before acquiring lock tends to be $370/2 = 185$ kHz. Average acquisition time is therefore 185 kHz/$\Delta \dot{f}$. Results are plotted in Figure B-5. Note that average search time, at strong signals, is approximately 15 seconds. This long time is directly attributable to the narrow-loop bandwidth required by the -135-dbm threshold.

Vehicle acceleration causes the Doppler frequency to change, and a dynamic acceleration error is caused thereby, of magnitude

$$\theta_a = \sin^{-1}\left(\frac{\Delta \dot{\omega}}{\omega_n^2}\right) = \sin^{-1}\left(\frac{2\pi \dot{f}_d}{\omega_n^2}\right) \qquad (4\text{-}19a)$$

where $\dot{f}_d$ is the Doppler rate. A plot of dynamic error versus signal strength is shown in Figure B-6 for several Doppler rates.

We now calculate the values for some of the loop components. A typical phase detector may have a gain factor of 3 volts per radian (K_d) and a

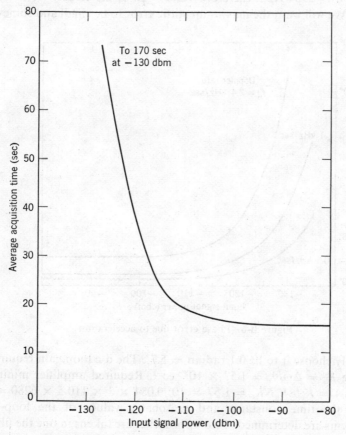

Figure B-5   Average acquisition time. Assumptions: 1. Total search range = 370 kHz. 2. Average acquisition time is one half of time needed to sweep total search range. 3. Sweep rate is $\Delta\dot{f}_{90}$ or $\dfrac{1}{2}\left(\dfrac{\omega_n^2}{2\pi}\right)$, whichever is least.

crystal VCO at 20 MHz can be expected to have a response of 1 kHz per volt. The VCO gain constant is therefore $K_o = 2\pi \times 1000 = 6280$ rps/volt. Because of the frequency multipliers, the effective VCO gain constant is $NK_o = 110.5 \times 6280 = 6.94 \times 10^5$.

Effective d-c gain of the loop is $K_v = \alpha A K_d N K_o$, where α is the limiter suppression factor and A is the d-c gain of any amplifier used in the loop.

Earlier it was found that at threshold $\alpha = 0.084$. Some value for A must now be found.

To this end it will be remembered that the static phase error due to frequency offset is $\theta_v = \Delta\omega/K_v$ (4-4a). Specifications call for a tracking range of ± 250 kHz; therefore $\Delta\omega = 2\pi \times 2.5 \times 10^5 = 1.57 \times 10^6$ rad/sec. We will want the maximum static error to be small and somewhat

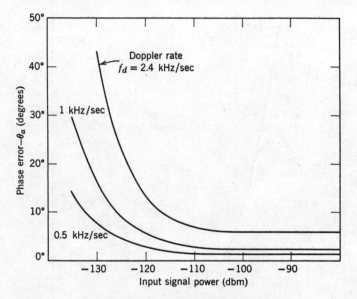

Figure B-6   Phase error due to acceleration.

arbitrarily choose it to be 0.1 radian $= 5.7°$. The d-c loop gain required is therefore $K_v = \Delta\omega/\theta_v = 1.57 \times 10^7$ sec^{-1}. Required amplifier minimum gain is $A = K_v/\alpha K_d N K_o = 1.57 \times 10^7/0.084 \times 3 \times 110.5 \times 6280 = 90$.

Next, the time constants and reasonable values of the loop-filter components are determined. Two approaches are taken; in one the filter is inserted between the phase detector and the amplifier in order to have a passive-filter loop. In the other the amplifier is used with the filter components connected in a feedback network to realize an active-filter loop.

Equation 2-10 relates the time constants to gain, natural frequency, and damping. If $\tau_1 \gg \tau_2 \gg 1/K_o K_d$ (which proves to be true in this example), the expressions for the passive filter in (2-10) will simplify to the same form shown for the active filter. By rearranging the equations, we arrive at formulas for the two time constants:

$$\tau_1 = \frac{K_o K_d}{\omega_n{}^2} \qquad \tau_2 = \frac{2\zeta}{\omega_n}$$

Damping at threshold has already been chosen as $\zeta = \frac{1}{2}$, and the noise bandwidth has been chosen as 56 Hz. Using (3-12) (or Figure B-2) we find that the natural frequency at threshold is $\omega_n = 112$ rad/sec. The smaller time constant is immediately found as $\tau_2 = 2 \times \frac{1}{2}/112 = 0.0089$ sec for both the passive and the active filter.

Before finding τ_1 we must first interpret the gain terms in (2-10) in a correct manner. When the expressions in (2-10) were derived, no account was taken of the limiter suppression factor, of frequency multiplication of the VCO, or of the presence of a d-c amplifier (at least in the passive filter). It has been indicated elsewhere in this book that the effective phase-detector gain factor is αK_d and the effective VCO gain is $N K_o$; we must now account for the d-c amplifier. For an active filter, reference to Figure 2-2 shows that the amplifier gain does not enter into the time constant calculations, whereas for the passive case we may regard it as a further multiplier on the VCO gain; that is, for the passive filter the effective VCO gain should be ANK_o.

With a passive filter, we find

$$\tau_1 = \frac{1.57 \times 10^7}{(112)^2} = 1250 \text{ sec}$$

whereas the active filter yields a value of

$$\tau_1 = \frac{1.75 \times 10^5}{(112)^2} = 13.9 \text{ sec}$$

Suppose R_1 (see Figure 2-2) is chosen to be 1 megohm. Then in the passive filter we require $C = 1250$ microfarads and $R_2 = 7.1$ ohms. These are not practical values. In the active filter the same choice of R_1 leads to $C = 13.9$ microfarads and $R_2 = 635$ ohms. The moral that emerges from this calculation is that if a d-c amplifier is used (to obtain sufficient d-c loop gain) it will often be advisable to incorporate the amplifier into an active loop filter. Otherwise, the filter components may take on highly inconvenient values, particularly if loop bandwidth is small.

Appendix C

Nomenclature

A Gain of d-c amplifier
B_i Bandwidth of filter preceding phaselock loop, hertz
B_L Loop noise bandwidth, hertz
B_{LT} Threshold value of B_L, hertz
D Modulation index of angle-modulated signal
f Frequency, hertz
$F(s)$ Transfer function of loop filter
$H(s)$ Phase transfer function of loop, θ_o/θ_i
J An oscillator noise parameter
K_d Phase-detector gain factor, volts per radian
K_o VCO gain, radians per (second) (volt)
K_v D-c loop gain, $K_o K_d F(0)$, dimensions of (seconds)$^{-1}$
L Limiter output voltage
N Frequency multiplication factor
$N(f)$ Noise spectral density, (volts)^2 per hertz
$n(t)$ Noise voltage
P_s Signal power, watts
P_n Noise power, watts
s Laplace complex variable
SNR   Power signal-to-noise ratio
$(\text{SNR})_i$ SNR at input
$(\text{SNR})_L$ SNR in loop
T_{av} Average time between skipping cycles, seconds
T_P Pull-in time, seconds
v_d, V_d Phase-detector output voltage
$W(f)$ Noise spectral density, watts per hertz
α Limiter signal suppression factor
α_T Threshold value of α
γ Oscillator noise spectral exponent
ζ Damping factor

θ_a Steady-state phase error due to frequency ramp input, radians

$\theta_e = (\theta_i - \theta_o)$ Phase error, radians

θ_i Input phase, radians

$\overline{\theta_{ni}^2}$ Equivalent mean-square input phase variance, (radians)^2

θ_o Output (VCO) phase, radians

$\overline{\theta_{no}^2}$ Mean-square VCO phase error due to output noise, (radians)^2

θ_v Steady-state phase error due to input frequency offset, radians

τ_1, τ_2 Time constants of loop filter, seconds

ω Radian frequency, radians per second

ω_B Bandwidth (3 db) of bandpass filter, radians per second

ω_m Modulation frequency, radians per second

ω_n Loop natural frequency, radians/second

$\Delta\omega$ Frequency offset or deviation, radians per second

$\Delta\omega_{DO}$ Dropout frequency, radians per second

$\Delta\omega_H$ Hold-in frequency, radians per second

$\Delta\omega_L$ Lock-in frequency, radians per second

$\Delta\omega_P$ Pull-in frequency, radians per second

$\Delta\omega_{PO}$ Pull-out frequency, radians per second

$\Delta\dot{\omega}$ Rate of change of input frequency, radians per second^2

Appendix D

Useful formulas

A set of useful formulas is presented here for the convenience of the reader who may wish to apply the material of this book to design problems. The number next to each formula is the equation number or the section number from which the formula was taken. Nomenclature is defined in the referenced section and in the list immediately preceding these formulas.

Loop Transfer Functions

General Loop

$$\frac{\theta_o(s)}{\theta_i(s)} = H(s) = \frac{K_o K_d F(s)}{s + K_o K_d F(s)} \qquad \text{(phase transfer)} \quad (2\text{-}6)$$

$$\frac{\theta_i(s) - \theta_o(s)}{\theta_i(s)} = \frac{\theta_e(s)}{\theta_i(s)} = \frac{s}{s + K_o K_d F(s)} \quad \text{(error response)} \quad (2\text{-}7)$$

Second-Order Loop*

Passive Filter

$$H(s) = \frac{s\left(2\zeta\omega_n - \dfrac{\omega_n^2}{K_o K_d}\right) + \omega_n^2}{s^2 + 2\zeta\omega_n s + \omega_n^2} \qquad (2\text{-}8)$$

$$\frac{\theta_e(s)}{\theta_i(s)} = \frac{s\left(s + \dfrac{\omega_n^2}{K_o K_d}\right)}{s^2 + 2\zeta\omega_n s + \omega_n^2} \qquad (2\text{-}12)$$

$$\omega_n = \left(\frac{K_o K_d}{\tau_1 + \tau_2}\right)^{1/2} \qquad \zeta = \frac{1}{2}\left(\frac{K_o K_d}{\tau_1 + \tau_2}\right)^{1/2}\left(\tau_2 + \frac{1}{K_o K_d}\right) \quad (2\text{-}10)$$

* See Figure 2-2 for description of loop filter.

166

Active Filter

$$H(s) = \frac{2\zeta\omega_n s + \omega_n{}^2}{s^2 + 2\zeta\omega_n s + \omega_n{}^2} \tag{2-9}$$

$$\frac{\theta_e(s)}{\theta_i(s)} = \frac{s^2}{s^2 + 2\zeta\omega_n s + \omega_n{}^2} \tag{2-11}$$

$$\omega_n = \left(\frac{K_o K_d}{\tau_1}\right)^{1/2} \qquad \zeta = \frac{\tau_2}{2}\left(\frac{K_o K_d}{\tau_1}\right)^{1/2} \tag{2-10}$$

Noise Bandwidth

$$B_L = \int_0^\infty |H(j\omega)|^2 \, df \quad \text{Hz (any-order loop)} \tag{3-12}$$

For high-gain, second-order loop

$$B_L = \frac{\omega_n}{2}\left(\zeta + \frac{1}{4\zeta}\right) \text{Hz} \tag{3-12}$$

If

$$\zeta = 0.707 \qquad B_L = 0.53\omega_n$$

If

$$\zeta = 0.5 \qquad B_L = 0.5\omega_n$$

Output Phase Jitter Due to Noise

$$\overline{\theta_{no}{}^2} = \frac{P_n}{P_s}\frac{B_L}{B_i} = \frac{W_i B_L}{P_s} = \frac{B_L}{B_i(\text{SNR})_i} \text{ rad}^2 \tag{3-13}$$

$$\theta_{no}{}^2 = \frac{1}{2(\text{SNR})_L} \text{ rad}^2 \tag{3-15}$$

$$(\text{SNR})_L = \frac{(\text{SNR})_i B_i}{2B_L} = \frac{P_s}{2B_L W_i} \tag{3-16}$$

(Above expressions for $\overline{\theta_{no}{}^2}$ are valid only if $(\text{SNR})_L > 10$.)

Noise Threshold

Unlock threshold: $(\text{SNR})_L = 1$ (0 db)
Acquisition threshold: $(\text{SNR})_L = 4$ (6 db)
(lower bounds for unmodulated carrier)

Average time to unlock (high-gain, second-order loop with $\zeta = 0.707$)

$$T_{\mathrm{av}} = \frac{2}{\omega_n} \exp\left[\pi(\mathrm{SNR})_L\right] \qquad (3\text{-}18)$$

Tracking Errors

Velocity Lag

$$\theta_v = \frac{\Delta\omega}{K_v} \text{ rad} \qquad (4\text{-}4a)$$

Acceleration Lag (second-order loop)

$$\theta_a = \frac{\Delta\dot\omega}{\omega_n^2} \text{ rad} \qquad (4\text{-}5)$$

For sinusoidal errors, see Figure 4-1; for transient errors, see Figures 4-2, 4-3, and 4-4.

Tracking Limits

Hold-in Range

$$\Delta\omega_{\mathrm{H}} = \pm K_v \text{ rad/sec} \qquad (4\text{-}18)$$

Maximum Locked Sweep Rate (second-order loop)

$$\Delta\dot\omega = \omega_n^2 \text{ rad/sec}^2 \qquad (4\text{-}20)$$

Maximum Frequency Step (pull-out of second-order loop)

$$\Delta\omega_{\mathrm{PO}} \approx 1.8\omega_n (\zeta + 1) \text{ rad/sec} \qquad (4\text{-}21)$$

Acquisition

Lock-in Range (second-order loop)

$$\Delta\omega_L \approx 2\zeta\omega_n \text{ rad/sec} \qquad (4\text{-}28)$$

Pull-in Range (high-gain, second-order loop)

$$\Delta\omega_{\mathrm{P}} \approx \sqrt{2}(2\zeta\omega_n K_v - \omega_n^2)^{1/2} \approx 2\sqrt{\zeta\omega_n K_v} \text{ rad/sec} \qquad (42\text{-}9,\ 30)$$

Pull-in Time (high-gain, second-order loop)

$$T_P \approx \frac{(\Delta\omega)^2}{2\zeta\omega_n{}^3} \tag{4-31}$$

For discussion of swept-frequency acquisition, see section 4-3. Maximum sweep rate for 90-percent probability of acquisition

$$\Delta\dot{\omega}_{max} = \frac{[1 - (SNR)_L^{-\frac{1}{2}}](\alpha/\alpha_o)\omega_{no}{}^2}{1 + d} \text{ rad/sec}^2 \tag{4-33}$$

$$(d = 0 \quad \text{if} \quad \zeta \geq 1)$$

Limiter

Signal-to-Noise Ratio

$$(SNR)_o \approx (SNR)_i \frac{1 + 2(SNR)_i}{4/\pi + (SNR)_i} \tag{5-3}$$

(See also Figure 5-1.)

Signal Suppression Factor

$$\alpha = \left(\frac{(SNR)_i}{4/\pi + (SNR)_i}\right)^{\frac{1}{2}} \tag{5-4}$$

Bibliography

The contents of this bibliography represent a fairly extensive survey of the existing literature concerning phaselock loop techniques and applications. Because of the many applications of phaselock loops, the bibliography has been divided into various classifications to simplify the location of a particular article. The classifications are listed in order below, the title of each classification indicating the subject material referenced.

Acquisition
Applications
Basic Operation
Circuits
Discriminators
Optimization
Oscillators
Phase detectors
Receivers
Threshold
Tracking

All of the references given previously are also listed in the bibliography.

Acquisition

Barnard, R. D., "Variational Techniques Applied to Capture in Phase-Controlled Oscillators," *BSTJ*, Vol. 41, pp. 227–256, January 1962.

Casson, W. H., and C. C. Hall, "New Phase-Tracking Demodulator Will Not Lock on Sidebands," *Electronics*, pp. 52–55, February 8, 1963.

Celinski, O., Z. J. Jelonek, and R. Syski, "Pulling Effect in Synchronized Systems," *Proc. IEE (London)*, Vol. 101, pp. 50–52, 1954.

Frazier, J. P., and J. Page, "Phase-Lock Loop Frequency Acquisition Study," *Trans. IRE*, **SET-8**, pp. 210–227, September 1962.

Goldstein, A. J., and C. J. Byrne, "Pull-in Frequency of the Phase-Controlled Oscillator," *Proc. IRE*, Vol. 49, p. 1209, July 1961.

Holtzman, J. M., and A. K. Rue, "Regions of Asymptotic Stability for Phase-Lock Loops," *Trans. IEEE*, **SET-10**, pp. 45–46, March 1964.

"A Phase-Locked Loop with Sideband Rejecting Properties," and "Sideband Lock Investigation," *JPL Space Programs Summary No.* 37–21, vol. III, pp. 76–83, May 31, 1963.

"Automatic Acquisition for Narrow Bandwidth, Phase-Locked Reference Loops," *JPL Space Programs Summary No.* 37–21, Vol. III, pp. 61–62, May 31, 1963.

"Strong Signal Sideband Discriminator," *JPL Space Programs Summary No.* 37–22, Vol. III, pp. 38–43, July 31, 1963.

Preston, G. W., and J. C. Tellier, "The Lock-in Performance of an AFC Circuit," *Proc. IRE*, Vol. 41, pp. 249–51, February 1953.

Richman, D., "DC Quadricorrelator: A Two Mode Sync System," *Proc. IRE*, Vol. 42, pp. 288–299, January 1954.

Robinson, E. M., "Acquisition Capabilities of Phase-Locked Oscillators in the Presence of Noise," *General Electric TTS No. R*60*DSD*11, Syracuse, N.Y., September 1960.

Tucker, D. G., "The Synchronization of Oscillators," *Electronic Engineering*, Vol. 16, pp. 26–30, June 1943.

Viterbi, A. J. "Acquisition and Tracking Behavior of Phase-Locked Loops," *JPL External Pub. No.* 673, July 14, 1959.

Applications

Benjaminson, A., "Phase-Locking Microwave Oscillators to Improve Stability and Frequency Modulation," *Microwave Journal*, pp. 88–92, January 1963.

———, "Phase-Locked Klystrons Simulate Doppler Radar," *Electronics*, pp. 44–46, April 19, 1963.

———, "Phase-Locked Microwave Oscillator Systems with 0.1 cps Stability," *Microwave Journal*, pp. 65–69, December 1964.

Bickmore, Robert W., "Adaptive Antenna Arrays," *Spectrum*, Vol. 1, pp. 78–88, August 1964.

Booton, R. C., "Demodulation of Wideband Frequency Modulation Utilizing Phase-Lock Technique," *Proc. 1962 Nat. Telem. Conf.*, Paper No. 4–6, May 1962.

Breese, M., R. Colbert, W. Rubin, and P. Sferrazza, "Phase-Locked Loops for Electronically Scanned Antenna Arrays," *Trans. IRE.*, **SET-7**, pp. 95–100, December 1961.

Burnett, E. E., "K_u-Band Phase-Locked System," *Proc. 1963 Nat. Winter Conv. on Military Electronics*.

Chadima, G. E., "Passive Satellite Tracking Radar Employing a 50% Duty Cycle and a Phase-Lock Receiver," *Proc. 1962 Nat. Symp, on Space Electronics and Telem.*, October 1962.

Choate, R. L., "Analysis of a Phase-Modulation Communication System," *JPL Progress Report PR*-30-21, October 8, 1959.

———, "Analysis of a Phase-Modulation Communications System," *Trans. IRE*, **CS-8**, pp. 221–227, December 1960.

———, "Design Techniques for Low-Power Telemetry," *Proc. 1962 Nat. Telem. Conf.*, Paper 3-1, May 1962.

————, and R. L. Sydnor, "Design of PM Communication Systems," *Trans. IRE*, **SET-8**, pp. 117–123, June 1962.

Clapp, J. K., and F. D. Lewis, "A Unique Standard-Frequency Multiplier," *IRE Nat. Convention Record*, Part 5, 1957.

Costas, J. P., "Synchronous Communications," *Proc. IRE*, Vol. 44, pp. 1713–1718, December 1956.

de Bey, L. G., "Tracking in Space by DOPLOC," *Trans. IRE*, **MIL-4,** pp. 332–334, April–July 1960.

Enloe, L. H., and J. L. Rodda, "Laser Phase-Locked Loop," *Proc. IEEE*, Vol. 53, p. 165, February 1964.

Gardner, Floyd M., "DOPLOC Uses Phase-Locked Filter," *Electronic Industries*, **18,** pp. 96–99, October 1959.

Hannan, W., and T. Olson, "An Automatic Frequency Controlled Phase Shift Keyed Demodulator," *RCA Rev.*, **22,** pp. 729–752, December 1961.

Jensen, G. K., "An Active Filter," *Naval Research Lab., Washington, D.C., Report No.* 4630, November 10, 1955.

Laughlin, C. R., "The Diversity-Locked Loop—A Coherent Combiner," *Trans. IEEE*, **SET-9**, pp. 84–91, September 1963.

Mathison, R. P., "Tracking Techniques for Interplanetary Spacecraft," *Proc. 1962 Nat. Telem. Conf.*, Paper 8-2, May 1962.

Nishimura, T., "The Mean-Squared Deviation of a Phase-Locked Loop Having a Triangular S-Curve," *JPL Space Programs Summary No.* 37-31, Vol. IV, pp. 311–315, February 28, 1965.

O'Sullivan, M. R., "Tracking Systems Employing the Delay-Lock Discriminator," *Trans. IRE*, pp. 1–7, **SET-8,** March 1962.

Peter, M., and M. W. P. Strandberg, "Phase Stabilization of Microwave Oscillators," *Proc. IRE*, Vol. 43, pp. 869–873, July 1955.

Pierce, John A., "Intercontinental Frequency Comparison by VLF Radio Transmission," *Proc. IRE*, Vol. 45, pp. 794–803, June 1957.

Poynter, R. L., and G. R. Steffensen, "Tunable High Stability Microwave Oscillator," *Rev. Sci. Inst.*, Vol. 34, pp. 77–82, January 1963.

Richman, D., "APC Color Sync for NTSC Color Television," 1953 *IRE Conv. Rec.*, Part 4.

Schlesinger, K., "Lock Oscillator for Television Synchronization," *Electronics*, Vol. 22, pp. 112–117, January 1949.

Spilker, J. J., Jr., "Delay-Lock Tracking of Binary Signals," *Trans. IEEE*, **SET-9,** pp. 1–12, March 1963.

————, and D. T. Magill, "The Delay-Lock Discriminator—an Optimum Tracking Device," *Proc. IRE*, Vol. 49, pp. 1403–1416, September 1961.

Stiffler, J. J., "The Squaring Loop Technique for Binary PSK Synchronization," *JPL Space Programs Summary No.* 37-26, Vol. IV, pp. 240–246, April 30, 1964.

————, "Phase-Locked Synchronization with Sinusoidal Signals," *JPL Space Programs Summary No.* 37-27, Vol. IV, pp. 208–212, June 30, 1964.

Strauch, R. G., "Phase Locking Millimeter Sources for Frequency Control," *Frequency*, 16–18, Prototype Issue, 1962.

Thirup, G., "The Application of Phase-Locking Techniques to the Design of Apparatus for Measuring Complex Transfer Functions," *Brit. IRE*, pp. 387–396, May 1960.

Victor, W. K., and M. H. Brockman, "The Application of Linear Servo Theory to the Design of AGC Loops," *JPL External Publication No.* 586, December 22, 1958; also *Proc. IRE*, Vol. 48, pp. 234–238, February 1960.

Viterbi, A. J., "System Design Criteria for Space Television," *Brit. IRE*, Vol. 19, pp. 561–570, September 1959.

Weaver, C. S., "Designing a Phase-Locked Loop as a Doppler Tracker," *Proc. IRE*, Vol. 50, p. 1992, September 1962.

Wendt, K. R., and G. L. Fredendall, "Automatic Frequency and Phase Control of Synchronization in Television Receivers," *Proc. IRE*, Vol. 31, pp. 7–15, January 1943.

Woodman, R. F., "A Phase-Locked Phase Filter for the Minitrack System," *NASA* (Goddard Space Flight Center) *Technical Note D*-1419, September 1962.

Basic Operation

Byrne, C. J., "Properties and Design of the Phase-Controlled Oscillator with a Sawtooth Comparator," *BSTJ*, Vol. 41, pp. 559–602, March 1962.

Cahn, C. R., "Piecewise Linear Analysis of Phase-Lock Loops," *Trans. IRE*, **SET-8**, pp. 8–13, March 1962.

Davenport, W. B., Jr., "Signal-to Noise Ratios in Band-Pass Limiters," *J. Appl. Phys.*, 24, pp. 720–727, June 1953.

Develet, Jean A., Jr., "The Influence of Time Delay on Second-Order Phase-Lock Acquisition Range," *Internat. Telem. Conf.*, pp. 432–437, London, 1963.

George, T. S., "Analysis of Synchronizing Systems for Dot-Interlaced Color Television," *Proc. IRE*, Vol. 38, pp. 124–131, February 1951.

Goldstein, A. J., "Analysis of the Phase-Controlled Loop with a Sawtooth Comparator," *BSTJ*, pp. 603–633, March 1962.

Gruen, W. J., "Theory of AFC Synchronization," *Proc. IRE*, Vol. 41, pp. 1043–1048, August 1953.

Jaffe, R., and E. Rechtin, "Design and Performance of Phase-Lock Loops Capable of Near-Optimum Performance Over a Wide Range of Input Signal and Noise Levels," *Trans. IRE*, **IT-1**, pp. 66–76, March 1955.

Labin, B., "Theory of Synchronization by Control of Phase," *Phillips Res. Rpts.*, Vol. 4, pp. 291–315, August 1949.

Lawhorn, R., and C. S. Weaver, "The Linearized Transfer Function of a Phase Locked Loop Containing an IF Amplifier," *Proc. IRE*, Vol. 49, p. 1704, November 1961.

Leek, R., "Phase-Lock AFC Loops," *Electronic and Radio Engineer*, pp. 141–146, April 1957, and pp. 177–183, May 1957.

Lindsey, W. C. "Investigation of Second-Order Phase-Locked Loops by Fokker-Planck Methods," *JPL Space Programs Summary No.* 37–30, Vol. IV, pp. 262–268, December 31, 1964.

McAleer, H. T., "A New Look at the Phase Locked Oscillator," *Proc. IRE*, Vol. 47, pp. 1137–1143, June 1959. Errata: **48**, p. 1771, October 1960.

Margolis, S. G., "The Response of a Phase-Locked Loop to a Sinusoid Plus Noise," *Trans. IRE*, **IT-3**, pp. 136–142, June 1957.

Martin, B. D., "The Pioneer IV Lunar Probe: A Minimum-Power FM/PM System Design," *Technical Report No.* 32–214, *JPL* March 1962.

"Phase-Locked Loop Study," Phase I of Project 2-520-1202, Motorola, Inc., Military Electronics Division, Scottsdale, Arizona, June 15, 1961, and Phase II of same project, December 15, 1961.

Preston, G. W., "Basic Theory of Locked Oscillators in Tracking FM Signals," *Trans. IRE*, **SET-5**, pp. 30–32, March 1959.

Pullen, K. A., "The Dynamic Characteristics of Phase-Lock Receivers," Report No. 1093, Ballistic Research Labs, Aberdeen Proving Ground, Maryland, January 1960.

Rechtin, E., "The Design of Optimum Linear Systems," *JPL External Publication No. 204*, April 1953.

Rey, T. J., "Automatic Phase Control: Theory and Design," *Proc. IRE*, Vol. 48, pp. 1760–1771, October 1960. Corrections in *Proc. IRE*, p. 590, March 1961.

Richman, D., "Color-Carrier Reference Phase Synchronization Accuracy in NTSC Color Television," *Proc. IRE*, Vol. 43, pp. 106–133, January 1954.

Schilling, D. L., "The Response of an Automatic Phase Control System to an FM Signal in the Presence of Gaussian Noise," *IEEE Int. Conv. Rec.*, Part 8, pp. 242–246, March 1963.

———, "The Response of an Automatic Phase Control System to FM Signals and Noise," *Proc. IEEE*, Vol. 51, pp. 1306–1315, October 1963.

———, and M. Schwartz, "The Response of an Automatic Phase Control System to FM Signals and Noise," *IRE Int. Conv. Rec.*, Part 8, pp. 111–121, March 1962.

Tausworthe, R. C., "New Calculation of Phase-Locked Loop Performance," *JPL Space Programs Summary No. 37-31*, pp. 292–300, February 28, 1965.

Viterbi, A. J., "The Effect of Sinusoidal Interference on Phase-Locked Loops," *JPL Section Rep. No. 8-583*, December 16, 1959

———, "Phase-Lock-Loop Systems," Chapter 8, *Space Communications*, Editor, A.V. Balakrishnan, McGraw-Hill, 1963.

Weaver, C. S., "A New Approach to the Linear Design and Analysis of Phase-Locked Loops," *Trans. IRE*, **SET-5**, pp. 166–178, December 1959.

Westlake, P. R., "Digital Phase Control Techniques," *Trans. IRE*, **CS-8**, pp. 237–246, December 1960.

Circuits

Edwards, K. A., O. Golubjatnikov, and D. J. Brady, "Transistor Phaselocked Oscillators," *AIEE Communications and Electronics*, pp. 1043–1051, January 1959.

Ordung, P. F., J. E. Gibson, and B. J. Shinn, "Closed Loop Automatic Phase Control," *Trans. AIEE*, **73**, pp. 375–381, September 1954.

Rechtin, E., "Design of Phaselock Oscillator Circuits," *JPL Section Rep. No. 8-566*, February 7, 1957.

Discriminators

Gilchriest, C. E., "The Application of Phase-Locked Loop Discriminators for Threshold Improvement and Error Reduction in FM/FM Telemetry," *JPL External Publication No. 364*, January 7, 1957.

———, "Design and Operations Handbook for Phase-Locked Loop Discriminator," *JPL Publication No. 127*, May 30, 1958.

———, "Application of the Phase-Locked Loop to Telemetry as a Discriminator or Tracking Filter," *Trans. IRE*, **TRC-4**, pp. 20–35, June 1958.

Lehan, F. W., "Telemetering and Information Theory," *Trans. IRE*, **TRC-2**, pp. 15–19, November 1954.

———, and R. J. Parks, "Optimum Demodulation," 1953 *IRE Nat. Conv. Rec.*, Part 8, pp. 101–103.

Lindsey, W. C., "Optimum Frequency Demodulation," *JPL Space Programs Summary No. 37–26*, Vol IV, pp. 227–234, April 30, 1964.

——, "Frequency Demodulation," *JPL Space Programs Summary No. 37–27*, Vol. IV, pp. 198–204, June 30, 1964.

——, "Threshold Characteristics in Phase-Locked Frequency Discriminators," *JPL Space Programs Summary No. 37–28*, Vol. IV, pp. 223–226, August 31, 1964.

McRae, D. D., "Phase-Locked Demodulation in Telemetry Receivers," *Proc. 1958 Nat. Symp. on Telem.*, Miami Beach, September 1958.

Martin, B. D., "Threshold Improvement in an FM Sub-Carrier System," *Trans. IRE*, **SET-6,** pp. 25–33, March 1960; Comment by J. J. Spilker appears in *Trans. IRE*, **SET-7,** p. 55, June 1961.

Miller, B. J., and L. L. Kocsis, "Phase-Lock Demodulators," National Electronics Conference, October 1962.

Runyan, R. A., "Factors Affecting Choice of Loop Filters in Phase-Locked Loop Discriminators," *Proc. 1959 Nat. Symp. on Space Electronics and Telem.*, Paper 9–1.

——, "Technique in the Application of Phase Lock Demodulators to Data Processing," *Proc. 1962 Nat. Telem. Conf.*, Paper 9–3.

Webb, J. A., "A Study in Demodulation Techniques," *Proc. Nat. Electronics Conf.*, 1961.

Optimization

Frenkel, Gabriel, "Oscillator Stability and the Second-Order Phase-Locked Loop," *Trans. IEEE*, **SET-10,** pp. 65–70, June 1964.

Goldstein, R., "The Minimization of Oscillator Noise," *JPL Research Summary No. 36–14*, pp. 61–63, May 1, 1962.

Jaffe, R. and E. Rechtin, "Design and Performance of Phase-Lock Loops Capable of Near-Optimum Performance Over a Wide Range of Input Signal and Noise Levels," *Trans. IRE*, **IT-1,** pp. 66–76, March 1955.

Nishimura, T., "Design of Phase-Locked Loop Systems with Correlated Noise Input," *JPL Space Programs Summary No. 37–26*, Vol. IV, pp. 234–240, April 30, 1964.

Oscillators

Anderson, T. C., and F. G. Merrill, "Crystal-Controlled Primary Frequency Standards: Latest Advances for Long-Term Stability," *Trans. IRE*, **I-9,** pp. 136–140, September 1960.

Attkinson, W. R., L. Fey, and J. Newman, "Spectrum Analysis of Extremely Low Frequency Variations of Quartz Oscillators," *Proc. IRE*, Vol. 51, p. 379, February 1963.

Barnes, J. A., and R. C. Mockler, "The Power Spectrum and Its Importance in Precise Frequency Measurements," *Trans. IRE*, **I-9,** pp. 149–155, September 1960.

Edson, W. A., "Noise in Oscillators," *Proc. IRE*, Vol. 48, pp. 1454–1467, August 1960.

Esposito, R., and J. A. Mullen, "Noise in Oscillators with General Tank Circuits," *IRE Conv. Rec.*, Part 4, pp. 202–208, 1961.

Felch, E. P., and J. O. Israel, "A Simple Circuit for Frequency Standards Employing Overtone Crystals," *Proc. IRE*, Vol. 43, pp. 596–603, May 1955.

Fey, L., W. R. Atkinson, J. Newman, and L. Malling, "Obscurities of Oscillator Noise," *Proc. IEEE*, Vol. 52, pp. 104–106, January 1964.

Golay, M. J. E., "Monochromaticity and Noise in a Regenerative Electric Oscillator," *Proc. IRE*, Vol. 48, pp. 1473–1477, August 1960.

Grivet, P., and A. Blaquiere, "Non-Linear Effects of Noise in Electronic Clocks," *Proc. IEEE*, Vol. 51, pp. 1606–1614, November 1963.

"VCO Stability," *JPL Research Summary No.* 36–3, pp. 52–53, June 15, 1960.

"RF Voltage-Controlled Oscillator Developments," *JPL Space Programs Summary No.* 37–15, Vol. III, pp. 34–36, May 31, 1962.

Malling, L. R., "Phase-Stable Oscillators for Space Communications, Including the Relationship Between the Phase Noise, the Spectrum, the Short-Term Stability, and the Q of the Oscillator," *Proc. IRE*, Vol. 50, pp. 1656–1664, July 1962.

Mullen, J. A., "Background Noise in Oscillators," *Proc. IRE*, Vol. 48, pp. 1467–1473, August 1960.

Real, R. R., "Direct Frequency Modulation of Crystal Controlled Transistor Oscillators," *Trans. IEEE*, CS-10, p. 459, December 1962.

Sann, K. H., "Phase Stability of Oscillators," *Proc. IRE*, Vol. 49, pp. 527–528, February 1961.

Smith, W. L., "Miniature Transistorized Crystal-Controlled Precision Oscillators," *Trans. IRE*, I-9, pp. 141–148, September 1960.

Strandberg, M. W. P., "Noise Spectrum of Phase-Locked Oscillators," *Proc. IRE*, Vol. 48, pp. 1168–1169, June 1960.

Sykes, R. A., W. L. Smith, and W. J. Spencer, "Performance of Precision Quartz-Crystal Controlled Frequency Generators," *Trans. IRE*, I-11, pp. 243–247, December 1962.

Victor, W. K., "The Evaluation of Phase-Stable Oscillators for Coherent Communication Systems," *JPL External Publication No.* 337, May 8, 1956.

———, "Minimum Bandwidths of Phase-Lock Loops Using Crystal-Controlled Oscillators," *JPL Section Report No.* 8–496, March 15, 1954.

Warner, A. W., "Design and Performance of an Ultra Precise 2.5 Mc Quartz-Crystal Unit," *BSTJ*, Vol. 34, pp. 1193–1217, September 1960.

Phase Detectors

Balodis, M., "Laboratory Comparison of TANLOCK and Phase-Lock Receivers," *Proc. Nat. Telem. Conf.*, Paper 5–4, 1964.

Chance, B., et al., *Waveforms*, MIT Rad. Lab. Series, Vol. 19, pp. 511–524, McGraw-Hill, New York, 1949.

Dishington, R. H., "Diode Phase Discriminators," *Proc. IRE*, Vol. 37, pp. 1401–1404, December 1949.

Golay, Marcel J. E., "The Application of Radio Interferometry to Extraterrestrial Metrology," *Trans. IRE*, SET-5, pp. 186–193, December 1959.

Highleyman, W. H., and E. S. Jacob, "An Analog Multiplier Using Two Field Effect Transistors," *Trans. IRE*, CS-10, pp. 311–317, September 1962.

Martin, T. B., "Circuit Applications of the Field-Effect Transistor," *Semicon. Prod.*, Vol. 5, Part I, pp. 33–39, February 1962; Part II, pp. 30–38, March 1962.

Pedersen, B. O., "Phase-Sensitive Detection with Multiple Frequencies," *Trans. IRE*, I-9, pp. 349–354, December 1960.

Robinson, L. M., "TANLOCK: A Phase-Lock Loop of Extended Tracking Capability," *Proc.* 1962 *Conv. on Military Electronics*, February 7–9, Los Angeles, California.

Stratemeyer, H. P., "A Low-Noise Phase Locked-Oscillator Multiplier," *Interim Proc. Symp. on Definition and Measurement of Short-Term Frequency Stability*, Part III, pp. 121–136, Goddard Space Flight Center, Greenbelt, Md., December 1964.

Williams, W. J., "Selection of Phase Sensitive Detectors for Space Radar," *Trans. IEEE*, **ANE-11,** pp. 230–234, December 1964.

Receivers

Brockman, M. H., H. R. Buchanan, R. L. Choate, and L. R. Malling, "Extraterrestrial Radio Tracking and Communication," *Proc. IRE*, Vol. 48, pp. 643–655, April 1960.

Hoffman, L. A., *Receiver Design and the Phase Lock Loop*, Aerospace Corp., El Segundo, California, May 1963. (Booklet prepared for Electronics and Space Exploration Technical Lecture Series, Sponsored by IEEE)

"L-Band Ground Transmit-Receive System," *JPL Space Programs Summary No. 37–18*, Vol. III, (DSIF), pp. 53–64, November 30, 1962.

"Mod. IV Planetary Radar Receiver, 2.388 Gc," *JPL Space Programs Summary No. 37–21*, Vol. III, (DSIF), pp. 49–61, May 31, 1963.

Martin, B. D., "A Coherent Minimum-Power Lunar Probe Telemetry System," *JPL External Publication No. 610*, May 1959.

———, "The Mariner Planetary Communication System Design," *Technical Report No. 32–85*, (Rev. No. 1) *JPL*, May 15, 1961.

Nelson, W. L., "Phase-Lock Loop Design for Coherent Angle-Error Detection in the Telstar Satellite Tracking System," *BSTJ*, Vol. 42, pp. 1941–1976, September 1963.

Richter, H., R. Stevens, and W. F. Sampson, "Microlock: A Minimum Weight Instrumentation System for a Satellite," *JPL External Publication No. 376*.

Sampson, W. F., and F. A. Ruegg, "Phase-Lock in Space Communications," *Proc. Nat. Symp. Space Elect. and Telem.*, Paper 1–3, September 1959.

Schwartz, L. S., "Phase-Lock for Aerospace Communications Receivers," *Space/Aeronautics*, pp. 71–75, February 1962.

Stevens, R., and M. H. Brockman, "Design and Performance of Deep Space Tracking and Telemetry System," *JPL External Publication No. 629*, May 1959.

Threshold

Develet, J. A., Jr., "An Analytic Approximation of Phase-Lock Receiver Threshold," *Trans. IEEE*, **SET-9**, pp. 9–11, March 1963.

———, "A Threshold Criterion For Phase-Lock Demodulator," *Proc. IEEE*, Vol. 51, pp. 349–356, February 1963. Correction in *Proc. IEEE*. p. 580, April 1963.

Lindsey, W. C., "Investigation of Second-Order Phase-Locked Loops by Fokker-Planck Methods," *JPL Space Programs Summary No. 37–30*, Vol. IV, pp. 262–268, December 31, 1964.

Schilling, D. L., and J. Billig, "On the Threshold Extension Capability of the PLL and the FDMFB," *Proc. IEEE*, Vol. 52, pp. 621–622, May 1964.

Spilker, J. J., Jr., "Threshold Comparison of Phase-Lock, Frequency-Lock and Maximum-Likelihood Types of FM Discriminators," presented at the IRE Wescon Conf., San Francisco, Calif., August 22–25, 1961.

Tausworthe, R. C., "New Calculation of Phase-Locked Loop Performance," *JPL Space Programs Summary No.* 37–31, Vol. IV, pp. 292–300, February 28, 1964.

Tikhonov, V. I., "The Effect of Noise on Phase-Lock Oscillation Operation," *Automatika: Telemekanika* **22,** 9 (1959).

———, "Phase-Lock Automatic Frequency Control Application in the Presence of Noise," *Automatika: Telemekanika* **23,** 3 (1960).

VanTrees, H. L., "A Threshold Theory for Phase-Locked Loops," *Technical Report No.* 246, Lincoln Lab., Mass. Inst. of Tech., August 22, 1961.

———, "Functional Techniques for the Analysis of the Non-Linear Behavior of Phase-Locked Loops," *Proc. IEEE*, Vol. 52, pp. 894–911, August 1964.

Viterbi, A. J., "Phase-Locked Loop Dynamics in the Presence of Noise by Fokker-Planck Techniques," *Proc. 7th Regional IEEE Conv.*, April 1963; also *Technical Report No.* 32–427, *JPL*, March 29, 1963.

———, "Phase-Locked Loop Dynamics in the Presence of Noise by Fokker-Planck Techniques," *Proc. IEEE*, Vol. 51, pp. 1737–1753, December 1963.

Tracking

Gupta, S. G. "Transient Analysis of a Phase-Locked Loop Optimized for a Frequency Ramp Input," *Trans. IEEE*, **SET-10,** pp. 79–83, June 1964.

Rue, A. K., and P. A. Lux, "Transient Analysis of a Phase Locked Loop Discriminator," *Trans. IRE*, **SET-7,** pp. 105–111, December 1961.

Sanneman, R. W., and J. R. Rowbotham, "Unlock Characteristics of the Optimum Type II Phase-Locked Loop," *Trans. IEEE*, **ANE-11,** pp. 15–24, March 1964.

Weaver, C. S., "Increasing the Dynamic Tracking Range of a Phase-Locked Loop," *Proc. IRE*, Vol. 4, pp. 952–953, May 1960.

———, "Thresholds and Tracking Ranges in Phase-Locked Loops," *Trans. IRE*, **SET-7,** pp. 60–70, September 1961.

Index